# Entropy for Biologists

*An Introduction
to Thermodynamics*

# Entropy for Biologists

*An Introduction
to Thermodynamics*

HAROLD J. MOROWITZ
*Yale University*

ACADEMIC PRESS  NEW YORK AND LONDON

Credits:

p.  xi: Reprinted with permission from H. B. Callen, "Thermodynamics." Wiley, 1960.

p.   1: From "The Poetry of Robert Frost," edited by Edward Connery Lathen. Copyright 1923 by Holt, Rinehart and Winston, Inc. Copyright 1951 by Robert Frost. Reprinted by permission of Holt, Rinehart and Winston, Inc.

p.   7: Reprinted with permission from "The Story of Nineteenth-Century Science," Henry Smith Williams. Harper and Brothers, 1901.

p.  31: Reprinted with permission from "The Nature of Thermodynamics," P. W. Bridgman. Harvard University Press, 1941.

p.  45: Reprinted with permission from "The Two Cultures: & A Second Look," C. P. Snow. Cambridge Univ. Press, 1959.

p.  73: Reprinted with permission from "What is Life?" Erwin Schrödinger. Cambridge Univ. Press, 1944.

p. 105: Reprinted with permission from "Symposium on Information Theory in Biology," Henry Quastler. Copyright 1958, Pergamon Press.

p. 133: Reprinted with permission from "Milton's Ontology, Cosmogony and Physics," Walter Clyde Curry. Univ. of Kentucky Press, 1957.

p. 145: From "Chemistry and Cookery," A. L. MacLeod and E. H. Nason. Copyright 1937. By permission of McGraw-Hill Book Co.

ACADEMIC PRESS, INC.
111 Fifth Avenue, New York, New York 10003


United Kingdom Edition published by
ACADEMIC PRESS, INC. (LONDON) LTD.
Berkeley Square House, London W1X 6BA


LIBRARY OF CONGRESS CATALOG CARD NUMBER: 73-117633


PRINTED IN THE UNITED STATES OF AMERICA

*To Jo, Eli, Josh, Zach, and Noah*

# Table of Contents

# Table of Contents

*Table of Contents*

# Preface

*The peculiar multiplicity of formulation and reformulation of the basic thermodynamic formalism is responsible for the apparent complexity of a subject which in its naked form is quite simple.*

from "Thermodynamics"
H. B. CALLEN
Wiley, 1960

There are so many books on thermodynamics that an ecologically concerned author feels the need of an apologia for being the causative instrument behind great trees being felled to make the paper on which this book is printed. I wrote this work because of my conviction that thermal physics is of real significance in many areas of biology and many biologists are put off from the subject by the usual modes of presentation.

I first became aware of the problem in 1953 at the National Heart Institute when a group of distinguished kidney physiologists requested that a course in thermodynamics be included in the postgraduate training program that was being introduced. During subsequent years I have had a large number of conversations with biologists who have been unhappy over their understanding of physical chemistry in general and thermodynamics in particular. During a sabbatical spent at the University of Hawaii in 1967, a series of such conversations with Microbiology graduate students led to a weekly bull session which we called "Entropy for Biologists." The ideas for this book began to take more definite shape during those sessions. Upon my return to Yale I have had a chance to develop and work out some of these ideas while teaching the thermodynamics background for a theoretical course in biological energetics.

What has emerged from my many experiences with thermodynamics in biology is the feeling that a large number of biologists and biochemists are eager to learn about thermal physics but have a curious ambivalence in their attitude toward the subject. They dislike the methods of teaching which are often too formal, too mathematical, and too abstract with little reference to the empirical foundations of the subject. On the other hand there is the realization that in such diverse fields as membrane physiology, cellular energetics, ecological systems theory, and macromolecular configuration, the results are becoming increasingly opaque to persons unversed in the subtleties of entropy and free energy.

Given this background, I decided to write an introductory book for people in the life sciences who wish to master the concepts of thermal physics without being forced to a degree and rate of symbol manipulation which is foreign to their patterns of thought. Planning such an enterprise was far easier than carrying it out. The subject matter of physical chemistry is embedded in the language of mathematical physics. While it cannot be separated from that language, the language must be made more verbal, less condensed and more intuitive in order to relate it to a biological mode of thought. Therefore the student is only assumed to be familiar with elementary calculus including the derivative, the partial derivative, and the integral and to have an elementary notion of differential equations. Other mathematical ideas are developed as needed.

In writing this book stress has been on developing understanding of the underlying ideas rather than in developing techniques for solving problems. This is not a "how to" book; it is rather a "what's it all about" book. It is my hope that after completing this book the reader will have the self-assurance and tools to tackle the "how to" books necessary to apply thermodynamics specifically to his own branch of biology. The book is then primarily directed at those graduate and advanced undergraduate students of biology and biochemistry who wish to develop a sense of confidence about their understanding of the thermal physics which will be useful in pursuing their work. It may also prove useful to professionals who wish to bolster their knowledge in this area.

Parts or all of the manuscript were read by John Ryan, Thomas Terry, Arnold Bloom, and Vicki Melchior. Their comments are gratefully acknowledged. Additional thanks are due to Arnold and Vicki for help in reading proof, to Beverly Cedarbaum for a skilled job of manuscript typing, and to Josh Morowitz for computing Table I. Particular mention must be made of my consultant expert in demonology, Huey Wen Huang. Finally my special thanks to my wife and editorial assistant, Lucille Morowitz, whose contributions were so extensive that she was constantly in danger of becoming a coauthor.

# Entropy for Biologists

*An Introduction
to Thermodynamics*

# CHAPTER I

# Temperature

*Some say the world will end in fire,*
*Some say in ice.*
*From what I've tasted of desire*
*I hold with those who favor fire.*
*But if it had to perish twice,*
*I think I know enough of hate*
*To say that for destruction ice*
*Is also great*
*And would suffice.*

"Fire and Ice" by
ROBERT FROST

## A. INTRODUCTION

All of biological process begins with the capture of solar photons and terminates with the flow of heat to the environment. The association of thermal physics and biology is thus a natural one which has become even closer in recent years as biological energetics and energetic ecology have become major focal points in the life sciences. As it has become apparent that thermodynamics goes much deeper than the considera-

*1*

tion of steam engines associated with its historical beginnings, it has also become apparent that biology is at its roots a profoundly thermodynamic subject.

In initiating our inquiry into thermal physics, it is instructive to give some thought to the logical character of the statements we shall employ. The primary assertions are generally of four categories: definitions, empirical generalizations, postulates, and conclusions that can be logically inferred from the other three categories. Definitions are arbitrary, but serve to structure the subject and place emphasis on certain concepts. Thus when we say that kinetic energy is equal to $\frac{1}{2}mv^2$ ($m$ is the mass and $v$ the velocity of an object) we are defining "kinetic energy" and at the same time indicating that the quantity is of sufficient importance in the structure of the subject to deserve a name. Thus in principle we could take the quantity $3m^2v$ and assign it a name "momentamass," but such a definition would serve no purpose, as the quantity is without significance in the development of dynamics.

Empirical generalizations occur in all branches of science but appear to be of special significance in thermodynamics. They are inductive statements which should be based on a large number of observations and the absence of contradictory observations. An example of a generalization is the statement that no engine acting in a cycle can transform heat into work without causing other changes. The particular power of thermodynamic reasoning is that such a statement can form the basis of an elaborate and impressive intellectual superstructure.

Postulates are statements whose validity rests entirely on comparison between experiments and the predictions based on the postulates. Thus when we postulate that gases are made of very small molecules which interact on collision like hard elastic spheres, we are making statements which can ultimately be checked by deducing what the macroscopic properties of such a system would be. The validity of the postulates rests on the agreement between the observed behavior of gases and the predicted behavior of a collection of small hard spheres.

Conclusions depend on the acceptance of the rules of logic and mathematics and the application of these rules to statements of the other three logical types.

In fully understanding the subtleties of thermodynamic reasoning, it is important to preserve the above distinction in logical character among various types of primary statements. In the following pages this will be done by printing such statements in italics and following them by either (definition), (empirical generalization), (postulate), or (conclusion).

## B. Physiological Temperature

The concept of temperature seems a particularly appropriate place to begin a biologically oriented book on thermodynamics since the ideas of temperature are rooted in the physiological sensations of hot and cold. Indeed hotness and coldness allow us to establish a crude qualitative temperature scale since, *given two objects A and B within the range of hotness such that we can touch them, we can always say that A is hotter than B, A is colder than B, or A and B are indistinguishable with respect to hotness* (empirical generalization).

## C. Empirical Thermometers

The preceding notion can be extended by noting that *it has been observed that a number of mechanical and electrical properties vary in a regular way with the degree of hotness as determined by physiological temperature* (empirical generalization). Among these properties are the electrical resistance of wires, the volume of liquids, the pressure of gases at constant volume, the chirping rate of crickets, and the rates of chemical reactions. Those properties which vary in a monotonic way with the degree of hotness (always increase with increasing temperature or always decrease with increasing temperature) can be used to construct an empirical thermometer, that is, we can use the measure of the property as the measure of the temperature. The most familiar example is a mercury-in-glass thermometer, where the length of the mercury column is a monotonic increasing function of physiological temperature, such that we can use the measure of length as some kind of numerical measure of the temperature. Such an empirical thermometer can then be placed in contact with an object and the empirical temperature determined. This use of empirical thermometers requires one further statement. *When two objects are kept in physical contact for a sufficient period of time they come to the same temperature, that is, they become indistinguishable with respect to degree of hotness* (empirical generalization). The existence of an empirical thermometer allows us to measure temperature, although the measure is on some completely arbitrary scale.

Using the empirical thermometer allows the discovery of temperature fixed points. We observe that *pure ice–water mixtures at one atmosphere pressure always give the same reading on a given empirical thermometer* (empirical generalization). Similarly, we observe that *all pure boiling water samples at one atmosphere pressure give the same reading on a given empirical thermometer* (empirical generalization). We may then use boiling water and melting ice as temperature fixed points and adjust all empirical thermometers to agree at these fixed points. If we call the ice temperature $\theta_i$ and the boiling-water temperature $\theta_i + 100$, we can divide the intermediate measure into 100 equal divisions. Setting $\theta_i = 0$ yields the conventional centigrade scale. Note that different empirical thermometers which are set to give the same readings at the boiling and freezing point will not necessarily be in agreement at any intermediate temperatures. Indeed each empirical thermometer establishes its own temperature scale.

Among the great variety of possible empirical thermometers, one class has been of particular utility in developing more theoretically founded notions of temperature. This class can be designated "gas-law thermometers." *It is found for a number of gases under a wide variety of pressures that the pressure of the gas at constant volume and the volume at constant pressure both increase in a regular way with physiological temperature* (empirical generalization). Either pressure or volume is then a suitable parameter for the design of an empirical temperature scale. We may then construct a thermometer which consists of a constant-volume vessel filled with gas attached to a pressure gage.

## D. Gas-Law Thermometers

Given the existence of empirical thermometers, we can now carry out experiments on temperature-dependent properties of systems. One such set of experiments shows that *there is a group of gases* (*helium, neon, argon, etc.*) *for which the pressure at constant empirical temperature varies as a linear function of the concentration of gas in the vessel* (empirical generalization).

We can now begin to analyze a gas-law thermometer in the following way. The temperature measure $\theta$ of a constant-volume thermometer is by definition proportional to the pressure $P$, so what we may write

$$\theta = \alpha P \tag{1-1}$$

where $\alpha$ is some constant of proportionality. If the gas-law thermometer is filled with one of the ideal gases discussed in our preceding empirical generalizations, we then know that the constant of proportionality is inversely proportional to the concentration of gas in the thermometer. This may be formally written

$$\alpha = \left(\frac{1}{C}\right)\left(\frac{1}{R}\right) \tag{1-2}$$

where $1/R$ is a new constant of proportionality and the concentration $C$ is the number of moles of gas $n$ divided by the volume of the thermometer $V$:

$$C = \frac{n}{V} \qquad (1\text{-}3)$$

If we substitute Equations (1-2) and (1-3) into Equation (1-1) we get

$$PV = nR\theta \qquad (1\text{-}4)$$

This looks like the familiar form of the ideal gas law of Boyle and Charles'. It is, however, logically something quite different; it is a definition of the empirical temperature $\theta$ for a constant-volume, ideal-gas thermometer. Indeed we could have arrived at Equation (1-4) more abruptly by asserting that the quantity $PV$ is a monotonic increasing function of the physiological temperature, hence an empirical temperature may be established as a constant of proportionality times this quantity. The constant $R$ may now be determined by use of the temperature fixed points. If we build an empirical thermometer of known volume $V$ and amount of gas $n$, then we may measure the pressure at the boiling and freezing points of water, $P_b$ and $P_f$. The equations at these two temperatures may be written

$$P_b V = nR\theta_b \qquad (1\text{-}5)$$

$$P_f V = nR\theta_f \qquad (1\text{-}6)$$

If we subtract Equation (1-6) from (1-5) we get

$$\frac{(P_b - P_f)V}{(\theta_b - \theta_f)n} = R \qquad (1\text{-}7)$$

All quantities on the left-hand side of the equation can be measured except $\theta_b - \theta_f$. However, if we establish our temperature scale by calling this difference 100, then $R$ may be directly computed. Once $R$ has been established this empirical thermometer establishes a complete temperature scale.

The constant $R$ as discussed above applies only to the specific thermometer under consideration. To show that it is a universal constant, we need invoke Avogadro's law, which states that *equal volumes of different (perfect) gases at the same temperature and pressure contain the same number of molecules* (postulate based on certain empirical generalizations). Applying this result to Equation (1-4) for a number of ideal gases shows that $R$ must be a universal constant. It is called the gas constant and has the dimensions of energy over temperature. Its value has been determined as $8.31432 \times 10^7$ ergs per °C per mole. In other commonly used units it is given as 1.9869 cal per °C per mole.

Starting with a good working empirical thermometer, we can establish a further property of water. *There is only one temperature and pressure at which pure water can coexist in the solid, liquid, and vapor phases* (empirical generalization). This is known as the triple point of water and is a convenient fixed point for very precise calibration in thermometry. If we call the temperature at the critical point $\theta_c$, then we can write Equation (1-5) as

$$R = \frac{P_c V}{\theta_c n} \tag{1-8}$$

Thus a single fixed point suffices to determine $R$ and establish an unambiguous gas-law temperature scale. The internationally agreed upon value of the triple point of water is 273.16°. The choice of this value is in principle completely arbitrary and establishes the size of a degree in the final temperature scale. In fact the choice was made to preserve agreement with the centigrade scale. When we refer to empirical temperature, unless otherwise stated we will mean the temperature of a perfect-gas thermometer calibrated at the $\theta_c$ value given above.

## PROBLEMS

1.  The density of water reaches a maximum value somewhere between the freezing and boiling point (4°C). Why would the density of water be a poor measure for an empirical thermometer?

2.  An enzyme preparation loses half its activity in 4 min at the boiling point of water. At the freezing point it loses half its activity in 4 months. Discuss an empirical thermometer which uses rate of enzyme inactivation as a measure of temperature.

3.  Why would the chirping rate of crickets be a poor parameter for an empirical thermometer?

4.  How would you construct an empirical thermometer which uses Brownian motion to measure temperature? Can you suggest why this would be an especially fundamental measurement of temperature?

5.  If the temperature of the critical point of water had arbitrarily been chosen to be 100°, what would be the value of $R$, the gas constant?

# CHAPTER II

# Energy

*It was just five years later, in 1842, that Dr. Julius Robert Mayer, practicing physician in the little German town of Heilbronn, published a paper in Liebig's* Annalen *on " The Forces of Inorganic Nature," in which not merely the mechanical theory of heat, but the entire doctrine of conservation of energy, is explicitly if briefly stated. Two years earlier, Dr. Mayer, while surgeon to a Dutch India vessel cruising in the tropics, had observed that the venous blood of a patient seemed redder than venous blood usually is observed to be in temperate climates. He pondered over this seemingly insignificant fact, and at last reached the conclusion that the cause must be the lesser amount of oxidation required to keep up the body temperature in the tropics. Led by this reflection to consider the body as a machine dependent on outside forces for its capacity to act, he passed on into a novel realm of thought, which brought him at last to independent discovery of the mechanical theory of heat, and to the first full and comprehensive appreciation of the great law of conservation. Bloodletting, the modern physician holds, was a practice of very doubtful benefit, as a rule, to the subject; but once, at least, it led to marvellous results. No straw is so small that it may not point the receptive mind of genius to new and wonderful truths.*

*Here, then, was this obscure German physician, leading the humdrum life of a village practitioner, yet seeing such visions as no human being in the world had ever seen before.*

from
" The Story of Nineteenth-Century Science "
by Henry Smith Williams
Harper and Brothers, 1901

A. Mechanical Energy

As we move through this chapter and many portions of subsequent chapters the direct relevance of the material to biology may often seem obscure. We are trying to establish the underlying laws and physical theories upon which biology must ultimately stand. Relating these laws to the actual phenomena of biology is an ongoing process which occupies the attention of much biological research. We are here concerned with footings and foundations which may seem tedious to those concerned with the great complexity, fascination, and beauty of the superstructure. We are reminded of the wise dictum of René Descartes, who said "If, therefore, anyone wishes to search out the truth of things in serious earnest, he ought not to select one special science; for all the sciences are conjoined with each other and interdependent."

With the preceding in mind we turn our attention to the concept of energy, which has been the dominant and unifying theme of physics for the past century. In recent years there has been a growing tendency to formulate biology in terms of energetic concepts, which is a return to the profoundly biological roots of the approach of Helmholtz and Mayer to energy conservation in their work in the 1840's and 1850's.

The ideas of energy came from consideration of heat, of light, of electricity, and from many other clues. The concepts of energy conservation can, however, be most clearly and concisely elaborated in the framework of mechanics. We will therefore develop our introductory concepts of energy in terms of the mechanics of the motion of a single particle. From this introduction we will find it a relatively simple matter to generalize the concepts.

For simplicity in the mathematical development we will consider a particle that is free to move in one dimension only, along the $x$ axis. The argument can easily be extended to three dimensions and for those who desire a more rigorous treatment we develop the full argument in vector notation in Appendix I. We will assume that the reader is familiar with the notions of force, position, velocity, acceleration, and mass.

We then introduce the concept of work, which is given as follows: *The work done in moving a mass from one point to another is defined as the distance moved times the force directed along the line of motion* (definition). Since the force may change along the path, we must use differentials and then sum up to get the total work. In one dimension we can state the previous definition in mathematical notation as

$$dW = F\,dx \qquad (2\text{-}1)$$

where $F$ represents the magnitude of the force directed along the axis. The amount of work done in moving an object from point $x_1$ to point $x_2$ is then given by

$$W_{12} = \int_{x_1}^{x_2} F \, dx \tag{2-2}$$

*For purely mechanical systems with no friction $W_{12}$ depends just on the end points $x_1$ and $x_2$ and is independent of the detailed way of getting from $x_1$ to $x_2$ (empirical generalization). Such systems are called con-* servative systems and they constitute the subject material of pure mechanics.

The idea of a frictionless mechanical system may at first sight seem like too much of an abstraction to be useful; nevertheless in celestial mechanics we actually encounter systems where to a very high order of approximation friction can be ignored. The theory of planetary orbits has been a very strong confirmation of the basic mechanics of conservative systems.

## B. CONSERVATION OF ENERGY

The empirical generalization just stated imposes strong mathematical limitations on the function $F$ and in fact requires the first equality in the following equation:

$$F = \frac{dW}{dx} = -\frac{dV}{dx} \tag{2-3}$$

For mathematical convenience we often do not use the function $W$, but use the negative of $W$, which we designate as $V$. *$V$ is called the potential, and forces which conform to Equation (2-3) are said to be derivable from a potential* (definition). *All of the usual forces of mechanics and electrostatics are derivable from a potential* (empirical generalization).

We can now extend our analysis by introducing Newton's second law of motion, which states that the force on a body is equal to the mass of the body times its acceleration, or in mathematical terms

$$F = m \frac{d^2 x}{dt^2} \tag{2-4}$$

It has been pointed out that Newton's second law is a definition of force as that which accelerates a material body. The law assumes definite content only when we are able to specify the force or potential as a function of the coordinate. For readers interested in these problems of the foundations of mechanics, we suggest referring to Chapter 3 of *Foundations of Physics* by R. B. Lindsay and H. Margenau (John Wiley and Sons, New York, 1936).

We next proceed to calculate the change of potential in going from $x_1$ to $x_2$. To carry this out, we start with Equation (2-1) and remember that $dW = -dV$; we then substitute Newton's law [Equation (2-4)] for the force and we have

$$-dV = m \frac{d^2x}{dt^2} dx \qquad (2\text{-}5)$$

To get the change of potential, we must integrate Equation (2-5) from the point on its path $x_1$ to the point $x_2$. If we remember that the acceleration is the derivative of the velocity, we get

$$\int_{x_1}^{x_2} -dV = m \int_{x_1}^{x_2} \frac{dv}{dt} dx = m \int_{x_1}^{x_2} dv \frac{dx}{dt} = m \int_{x_1}^{x_2} v \, dv \qquad (2\text{-}6)$$

The last two equalities in Equation (2-6) represent formal rearrangement of the symbols to get the expression in more convenient form to integrate. When we finally integrate Equation (2-6) we get

$$V(x_1) - V(x_2) = \tfrac{1}{2}mv^2(x_2) - \tfrac{1}{2}mv^2(x_1) \qquad (2\text{-}7)$$

Equation (2-7) may be rewritten in a form that makes its meaning more clear,

$$V(x_1) + \tfrac{1}{2}mv^2(x_1) = V(x_2) + \tfrac{1}{2}mv^2(x_2) \qquad (2\text{-}8)$$

The quantity $V + \tfrac{1}{2}mv^2$ thus has the same value at the point $x_2$ as at the point $x_1$. Since these are arbitrary points along the path, the quantity $V + \tfrac{1}{2}mv^2$ is thus an invariant or constant of motion. *The term $\tfrac{1}{2}mv^2$ is known as the kinetic energy* (definition) and $V$ has already been designated as the potential or potential energy. *The quantity $V + \tfrac{1}{2}mv^2$ is designated the total energy of a particle* (definition). We have thus shown that the total energy of a particle is invariant and consists of the sum of two terms, the potential energy and the kinetic energy. The potential energy is a function of the coordinates only. It is considered to be the stored energy that a particle possesses by virtue of the work which had to be done to bring it to its present position. The kinetic energy is a function of the velocity only. It is thus the energy of motion, the amount of energy possessed by a particle by virtue of its moving at velocity $v$. Equation (2-8) states that as the particle moves along its trajectory potential energy may be converted to kinetic energy and vice versa, but the sum of the two quantities remains constant. Equation (2-8) is the law of conservation of mechanical energy and is the cornerstone for many developments in physics.

The dimensions of kinetic energy are mass times velocity squared or mass times length squared divided by time squared. The dimensions of work or potential energy are force times distance. Force is given dimensionally as mass times acceleration or mass times distance divided by time squared. Potential energy thus has the dimensions of mass times distance squared divided by time squared and is dimensionally the same as kinetic energy, as we would expect from Equation (2-8). In cgs units mass is measured in grams and force in dynes, which is that force which will accelerate a one-gram mass by one centimeter per second squared. Energy is measured in ergs, the work done by a one-dyne force acting through one centimeter.

We may sum up the foregoing as follows. Energy is a measure of a system's capacity for doing work. For conservative mechanical systems, this is the sum of two components: the kinetic energy, which the system possesses by virtue of its motion, and the potential energy, which results from its configuration. Work in the mechanical sense is the displacement of any body against an opposing force, or the product of the force times the distance displaced.

Let us consider a few examples. If we have a weight suspended from the ceiling, it possesses potential energy; that is, it can be connected by a set of pulleys to any mechanical system and, when released, it will do work. If we release the weight, it will fall to the ground and at the moment of striking the ground it still possesses energy. For example, we could have it strike the end of a lever and perform work. That energy would not result from the position of the object but from its movement with some velocity $v$. This energy is kinetic energy. If we consider the weight at some point in its fall intermediate between ceiling and floor, we see that some of the energy is potential and some kinetic. The law of conservation of mechanical energy states that the total of potential and kinetic energy is constant. As the body falls, potential energy is converted to kinetic energy, but the total energy remains unaltered.

For the next example visualize a weight hanging from a metal spring. If we displace the weight downward, we do work. That is, we must exert a force over some distance. The system now possesses potential energy as a result of its configuration. If we release the weight, it will move upward until the spring is compressed; it will then reverse its motion and move downward until the spring is stretched and continued to execute the familiar periodic vibration of a spring. At the beginning, the energy is all potential, but as motion begins there is a conversion to kinetic energy. When the spring is compressed the motion ceases and the energy is reconverted to potential energy, which is again transformed into kinetic energy as the weight moves downward. The law of the conservation of mechanical energy predicts that the total energy will be constant, and in this case it constantly shifts from kinetic to potential. If the conservation of mechanical energy were the only law governing this situation, the oscillation once started would persist forever; that it does not is related to frictional forces and the production of heat, which will be discussed later.

The previous development of the law of conservation of energy is based on macroscopic laws. There is no reason to suggest that these laws would not hold at a microscopic (molecular) level, but a difficulty enters when we try to account for energy at this level. An ordinary piece of matter contains an enormous number of atoms, so that any detailed accounting of the dynamical variable becomes clearly impossible. We also know that in any real situation there are frictional processes in which macroscopic mechanical energy is converted into energy in microscopic modes. Therefore, the methods of mechanics are inadequate to a wide range of physical problems in which we need to be concerned with the energy distribution among a large number of molecules. Three closely related methods are used by physicists and chemists to deal with these situations where detailed mechanical treatments are not possible. These are thermodynamics, statistical mechanics, and kinetic theory. Thermodynamics uses only macroscopic quantities and derives certain equations which must obtain between experimentally determined quantities; relations between variables which are called phenomenological relations. Statistical mechanics considers certain average properties of systems which we can deal with in spite of our ignorance of the mechanical details of individual molecules. To date this type of averaging has been worked out almost exclusively for equilibrium systems, so that statistical mechanics has not been very useful in the study of transport properties such as diffusion and heat flow. Kinetic theory deals with mechanical model systems at a molecular level and the appropriate averaging over the molecules to predict measurable properties. While it can thus be used for transport properties, it suffers from the difficulty that for all real cases the mathematics becomes exceedingly complex and often impossible.

Each of the three branches of thermal physics thus has advantages and disadvantages and they can best be studied together since the various approaches interact and supplement each other. Our understanding of various concepts is thus improved by examining their development in the three disciplines. In addition in actual problems we are often called upon to decide the best method of approach and it is well to realize that we may have a choice so that we can choose the best available technique.

## C. THERMAL ENERGY

With the previous considerations of mechanical energy in mind we can generalize our point of view and turn to the concept of thermal energy. *It is frequently observed that for real systems the conservation of mechanical energy [Equation (2-8)] fails to hold. Such situations are almost invariably associated with a rise in temperature somewhere in the system* (empirical generalization). For example, if a car is traveling along a road at 30 mph, it has a certain kinetic energy ($\frac{1}{2}mv^2$). If on a level surface we apply the brakes and the car comes to a stop, the kinetic energy goes to zero and no potential energy appears. The brakes heat up in this process. Equation (2-7) makes no mention of temperature, so that mechanics by itself provides no method of dealing with the preceding situation. Temperature does not enter into the formulation of mechanics, so new methods must be devised for systems involving friction or dissipative forces.

The loss of mechanical energy, with the subsequent rise in temperature, was a most important observation in the historical development of thermodynamics. In 1798 Benjamin Thompson, Count Rumford, carried out his classical experiments on the boring of cannon. He showed in a rough way that the heat produced was proportional to the total work done. He wrote, " It is hardly necessary to add, that any thing which any insulated body, or system of bodies, can continue to furnish without limitation, cannot possibly be a material substance: and it appears to me to be extremely difficult, if not quite impossible, to form any distinct idea of any thing capable of being excited and communicated, in the manner the heat was excited and communicated in these experiments, except it be Motion." This is usually cited as an example of the importance of this type of process to the formulation of thermodynamics. We are now aware, of course, that the mechanical energy "lost" in dissipative processes appears as kinetic energy of molecules and that the temperature and average kinetic energy of atoms are very closely related. This result goes beyond thermodynamics and is related to a more detailed view of the nature of matter.


## PROBLEMS

1. A metal spring is compressed, requiring an amount of work $W$. The spring is tied in the compressed state and dropped into a vat of acid, which dissolves it. What happens to the potential energy $W$?

2. Consider a car which is subject to the following two types of collision: (a) It collides with a rigid wall with an impact velocity of 40 mph. (b) It moves at 20 mph and collides with a car moving directly at it with a velocity of 20 mph. Which collision is likely to be more damaging to the first car and why?

3. A 1-gm mass strikes the earth's surface at 1000 cm/sec and makes an elastic collision. How high up will it rebound? (Note: the potential energy in the earth's gravitational field is $mgh$, where $m$ is the mass, $g$ the gravitational acceleration, 980 cm/sec$^2$, and $h$ the height above the surface.)

4. A 2-kg bird leaves the ground and flies to a height of 50 meters, where it attains a velocity of 3 meters/sec. What is the minimum amount of metabolic energy that the bird must have expended?

# CHAPTER III

# Introduction to Kinetic Theory

*It is sweet to dance to violins*
*When Love and Life are fair:*
*To dance to flutes, to dance to lutes*
*Is delicate and rare:*
*But it is not sweet with nimble feet*
*To dance upon the air!*

OSCAR WILDE
"The Ballad of Reading Gaol"

In order to gain more insight into the concept of thermal energy, it is well to consider the kinetic theory of gases, an approach which makes contact between mechanics and the thermal view of matter. In this chapter we introduce the simplest notions of kinetic theory so that we can discuss temperature in terms of molecular mechanics.

We shall proceed by making a series of postulates about the nature of matter, deducing the consequences of these postulates, and checking these results against experiment. In this context we introduce the following postulates:

P(1)   Perfect monatomic gases are made up of very small spherical molecules.

P(2)   At normal pressures the molecules occupy only a small fraction of the total volume of the system.

P(3)   The molecules move rapidly and randomly in all directions. There is a state of the system (the equilibrium state) in which there is no net motion of the entire system, so that if we look at a small volume of gas, as many molecules have a velocity $v$ as have a velocity $-v$.

P(4)   Molecules interact with each other and with the walls only by elastic collisions involving short-range repulsive forces.

P(5)   The laws of Newtonian mechanics hold for the molecular system.

The postulates just presented introduce a number of new ideas that require explanation. The first of these is the notion of equilibrium, a concept that turns out to have a number of subtleties, and requires certain preliminary considerations. *First consider an infinite isothermal reservoir, which is an object very large in comparison to an experimental system we wish to study and has the property that an empirical thermometer gives the same reading regardless of where or when it is placed in the reservoir* (definition). An infinite isothermal reservoir is clearly an idealization in the sense that point masses and point charges are idealizations. Nonetheless, we can approach such a reservoir arbitrarily closely, a point stressed with great vigor by the manufacturers of incubators and refrigerators and other constant-temperature devices.

A second idealization is *an adiabatic wall, which is a structure through which no energy may flow.* Since we have not completed our discussion of energy, the adiabatic wall must stand as a somewhat vague concept. We have, however, noted the existence of potential, kinetic, and thermal energy, so that an adiabatic wall must, as a minimum, not permit the passage of these forms of energy. Since matter flow in general is accompanied by energy flow, it follows that an adiabatic wall must be impermeable to the flow of matter. As we shall later see an adiabatic wall is also an idealization which may be experimentally approached although never perfectly attained. We may for most purposes consider a rigid wall, which has no holes or pores and is a very good insulator with respect to heat flow.

If a system is placed in contact with an infinite isothermal reservoir and allowed to age for a very long time, it approaches the following conditions:

1.   The empirical temperature is uniform throughout (empirical generalization).

2. All measurable properties of the system become independent of time (empirical generalization).
3. The system can be completely described (macroscopically) in terms of a small number of parameters. If a system contains $n$ species of molecules, $n + 2$ parameters suffice to completely describe the system (empirical generalization).

A system of this type is designated an equilibrium system, or alternatively we designate it as being in an equilibrium state. The concept of equilibrium, while very awkward to talk about, is extremely fundamental to our understanding of thermal physics. Equilibrium states, because of their particular simplicity, are at the present time amenable to much more exact analysis than are nonequilibrium states.

The three conditions used to describe the equilibrium state require some further discussion. The uniformity of empirical temperature is subject to temperature fluctuations which become more and more significant as we look at smaller and smaller regions of the system. In taking a more microscopic point of view, we will later examine these fluctuations, which are themselves fundamental to the description of the system. The independence of parameters with time depends on the time scale that we use; that is, we may achieve equilibrium with respect to relatively rapid processes but not be in equilibrium with respect to slower processes. For example, consider a container with two moles of hydrogen gas and one mole of oxygen gas in contact with a reservoir at $0°C$. After a short time the system will be in apparent equilibrium. If, however, we continue the study of the system over a very long time, there will be a slow production of water. The final equilibrium state will contain almost no hydrogen and oxygen but will be almost entirely water. The initial equilibrium takes place in minutes or hours, while the final equilibrium may require years or centuries. For many purposes we can regard the initial equilibrium as a true equilibrium and treat the system accordingly.

Equilibrium may also be achieved by surrounding a system with adiabatic walls and allowing it to age in that condition for a long time. The previous three conditions apply to such a system, as do our other comments on the concept of equilibrium.

We next consider a detailed account of the mechanical features involved in a perfect-gas molecule colliding with a wall. When this process is understood we can use the postulates of kinetic theory to study the

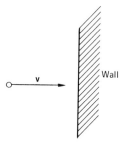

**Fig. 3-1.** Perfect gas molecule moving with velocity $v$ toward a rigid wall.

overall properties of perfect gases and ultimately to extend our under-standing of the temperature concept. Consider then a fixed, rigid wall being approached by a perfect-gas molecule at velocity $v$ as shown in Figure 3-1. For simplicity we assume that the velocity vector is in the $x$ direction and is perpendicular to the plane of the wall. Ideally, a perfect-gas molecule would act as a completely hard sphere; that is, no forces would exist between the molecule and the wall until the distance between the center of the sphere and the wall was $r$, the radius of the sphere. The force would then be repulsive and would assume a very high value, effectively infinity. The potential energy curve corresponding to this is shown in Figure 3-2. In fact, we need not employ such a completely idealized view but can assume a force field more nearly like that shown in Figure 3-3, which more closely represents what would happen at an actual wall. This problem can now be examined in terms of classical

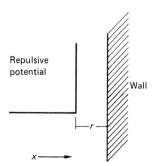

**Fig. 3-2.** Interaction potential between molecule and wall as a function of the distance between them, $x$. Hard sphere approximation is shown with $r$ equal to the molecular radius.

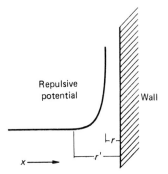

**Fig. 3-3.** Interaction potential between molecule and wall as a function of the distance between them, $x$. Actual case is shown where the repulsive force sets in at a distance $r'$, and the distance of closest approach is $r$.

mechanics, starting with the conservation of mechanical energy. For the moving gas molecule we can write the following equation:

$$\tfrac{1}{2}mv_0{}^2 = \tfrac{1}{2}mv(x)^2 + V(x) \tag{3-1}$$

As the particle approaches the wall it has a kinetic energy $\tfrac{1}{2}mv_0{}^2$ and no potential energy. As it gets into the force field work is done, the kinetic energy decreases, and the potential energy increases. Eventually a point $x$ is reached where $V(x) = \tfrac{1}{2}mv_0{}^2$; the energy is now all potential, the velocity falls to zero, and the particle has reached its point of closest approach to the wall. The repulsive force is still operative and the molecule now begins to move away from the wall. When it reaches the point where it originally entered the force field the velocity is now $-v_0$ and the energy is entirely kinetic. Assume that the particle enters the force field at time $t_1$ and leaves at time $t_2$. The average force on the wall during this time is by Newton's third law the negative of the force on the particle,

$$\bar{F} = \frac{1}{t_2 - t_1} \int_{t_1}^{t_2} -F \, dt \tag{3-2}$$

Equation (3-2) represents the general method of determining the time average of any quantity. If we now apply Newton's second law, we get

$$\bar{F} = \frac{-1}{t_2 - t_1} \int_{t_1}^{t_2} m \frac{d^2x}{dt^2} \, dt = \frac{-1}{t_2 - t_1} \int_{t_1}^{t_2} m \frac{dv}{dt} \, dt = -\int_{t_1}^{t_2} \frac{m \, dv}{t_2 - t_1} = \frac{2mv_0}{t_2 - t_1} \tag{3-3}$$

We have again used the fact that the acceleration $d^2x/dt^2$ is the time derivative of the velocity $dv/dt$. The final equality in the above equation comes about since $v(t_1)$ is $v_0$, and $v(t_2)$ is $-v_0$, as already indicated. The calculated value then represents the average force that one gas molecule exerts on the wall during the period they are in collision.

Return now to the postulates of kinetic theory and consider a perfect gas in a container having plane walls. Assume there are $B$ molecules in a container of volume $V$, or $B/V$ molecules per unit volume. These are small, hard spheres moving randomly in all directions with an average velocity $\bar{v}$. Consider next a plane wall of the container. At a distance $r$ from the wall construct an imaginary plane as in Figure 3-4. The num-

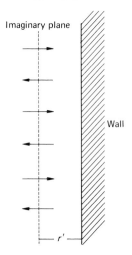

Imaginary plane

Wall

$r'$

**Fig. 3-4.** Molecules passing an imaginary plane a distance $r'$ from a rigid wall.

ber of molecules passing the plane from left to right in a given time is $\frac{1}{6}(B/v)\bar{v}$. This number is arrived at by assuming that $\frac{1}{3}$ of the molecules are moving in the $x$ direction, $\frac{1}{3}$ in the $y$ direction, and $\frac{1}{3}$ in the $z$ direction. Of those moving in the $x$ direction, $\frac{1}{2}$ are moving from right to left and $\frac{1}{2}$ are moving from left to right. Therefore $\frac{1}{2}$ of $\frac{1}{3}$, or $\frac{1}{6}$ of the molecules are moving toward the plane we wish to consider. Since the concentration of molecules is $B/V$, the quantity $\frac{1}{6}(B/V)$ is the concentration of molecules moving toward the plane we are considering.

The molecules reaching the plane in one second are those heading in the right direction which are within a distance of $\bar{v}$ times one second, which is just $\bar{v}$. That is, the velocity times time is distance, and, if the time is chosen as one second, the distance is numerically equal to the velocity. If we look at unit area of surface (for example, a one centimeter by one centimeter square), the molecules arriving in one second are contained in a rectangular parallelepiped of base $1 \times 1$ and height $\bar{v}$. The volume of this figure is $\bar{v}$, and the concentration of appropriately directed molecules is $\frac{1}{6}(B/V)$, therefore the number of molecules passing a unit area of the plane in a second is $\frac{1}{6}(B/V)\bar{v}$.

Each molecule is in contact with the wall from the time it passes the plane until the time it passes again in the opposite direction, having been reflected by the contact. This time is $t_2 - t_1$, and we have already calculated in Equation (3-3) the average force $F$ exerted on the wall during the contact. Per unit area of wall the average number of molecules in contact at any time is therefore

$$\frac{1}{6}\left(\frac{B}{V}\right)\bar{v}(t_2 - t_1)$$

and the force per unit area is

$$\frac{F}{A} = \frac{1}{6}\left(\frac{B}{V}\right)\bar{v}(t_2 - t_1)\bar{F} = \frac{1}{6}\left(\frac{B}{V}\right)\bar{v}(t_2 - t_1)\frac{2m\bar{v}}{t_2 - t_1} = \frac{1}{3}\frac{B}{V}m\bar{v}^2 \qquad (3\text{-}4)$$

Note that the quantity $t_2 - t_1$ drops out of the final expression. This quantity would be very difficult to calculate since it depends on the detailed nature of the force field in the neighborhood of the wall. Equation (3-4) shows that the general result is independent of this detail. The force per unit area of wall is, however, simply the pressure exerted on the wall by the gas, which we have already designated as $P$, so that Equation (3-4) can be written as

$$P = \frac{1}{3}\left(\frac{B}{V}\right)m\bar{v}^2 \qquad (3\text{-}5)$$

We can now compare Equation (3-5) with Equation (1-4) since they both relate to gas pressure,

$$PV = nR\theta = \tfrac{1}{3}Bm\bar{v}^2 \qquad (3\text{-}6)$$

The average kinetic energy of a gas molecule K.E. is equal to $\tfrac{1}{2}m\bar{v}^2$, and $B$ molecules are equal to $B/\mathcal{N}$ or $n$ moles, where $\mathcal{N}$ is Avogadro's number. Thus

$$\left(\frac{R}{\mathcal{N}}\right)\theta = \frac{2}{3}\text{ K.E.} \qquad (3\text{-}7)$$

The empirical temperature of a perfect-gas thermometer is thus directly proportional to the average kinetic energy of a molecule.

This result turns out to be more general than for perfect gases, so that under a wide variety of equilibrium conditions temperature is a measure of the average kinetic energy of the molecules making up the system. The ratio of the gas constant to Avogadro's number $R/\mathcal{N}$ is itself a constant $k$, usually called the Boltzmann constant. Equation (3-7) thus indicates that the average kinetic energy per molecule is equal to $\frac{3}{2}k\theta$, that is, the kinetic energy is three halves times the Boltzmann constant times the empirical temperature. For a perfect gas, temperature is therefore a straightforward measure of the average kinetic energy of translation per molecule.

The previous result can be generalized beyond perfect gases and beyond equilibrium situations. We will define the kinetic theory temperature $\phi$ as follows (Definition):

$$Bk\phi = \frac{2}{3}\sum_i \frac{1}{2} m_i v_i^2 \tag{3-8}$$

where the summation is over all molecules in the system. As already indicated, for a perfect gas at equilibrium $\phi = \theta$.

We are now able to assume a much more intuitive view of temperature at the molecular level. All matter is made of atoms and molecules. These building blocks are very small and are in constant motion as well as constant collision with each other. As a result of these processes there is a certain amount of kinetic energy which is rather uniformly distributed over the particles. The macroscopic notion of temperature is simply and directly related to the amount of kinetic energy associated with a given sample. The existence of an absolute zero of temperature in classical physics is then easy to understand, since it is that state where the particles have zero kinetic energy. Clearly, no lower temperature will be possible.

The idea of a temperature range for biological phenomena can also be viewed from this perspective. At low temperatures the molecules possess little energy and processes which require an activation energy are slowed way down. Above the normal temperature range the biological structures are subject to many high-energy collisions from neighboring molecules and this tends to break down the macromolecular configurations and leads to inactivation.

Inherent in this view is the notion that matter is not at all static, but when examined submicroscopically is in violent agitation. It is well to incorporate this thought into our ideas of biology since in the end it will give us a truer view of life at the molecular level.

## PROBLEMS

1. Using Avogadro's number as $6 \times 10^{23}$, calculate the mass of an $H_2$, an $N_2$, and an $O_2$ molecule.

2. Calculate the average velocity of $H_2$, $N_2$, and $O_2$ at 300° on the ideal gas scale.

3. Plot the average velocity of an $N_2$ molecule as a function of temperature between 0 and 600° on the ideal gas scale.

4. What is the total kinetic energy of a mole of oxygen gas at 300° on the ideal gas scale?

5. An organism consists of 1.3 gm of tissue (density 1.3 $gm/cm^3$) and has a float bladder containing 0.001 mole of $N_2$ gas. The organism is suspended in a lake (density 1) at 280° on the ideal gas scale. At what depth in the lake will the organism be stable with respect to floating up or sinking? Assume that the organism can adjust the float bladder volume to equalize internal and external pressure.

CHAPTER **IV**

# Total Energy

> *Now king David was old and stricken in years;*
> *and they covered him with clothes, but he could*
> *get no heat. Wherefore his servants said unto*
> *him: "Let there be sought for my lord the king*
> *a young virgin; and let her stand before the king,*
> *and be a companion to him; and let her lie in thy*
> *bosom, that my lord the king may get heat." So*
> *they sought for a fair damsel throughout all the*
> *borders of Israel, and found Abishag the Shu-*
> *nammite, and brought her to the king.*
>
> First Kings, 1.1–1.3

A. The Measurability of Energy

In the preceding chapters we have distinguished potential energy from kinetic energy and we have further distinguished the energy in macroscopic modes, which is accessible to study and measurement by the methods of mechanics, from the energy in microscopic modes, which is ultimately associated with the notion of temperature. In this chapter we will begin by a consideration of the total energy of a system which is isolated from the rest of the universe by a set of rigid adiabatic walls.

Since the considerations we have established preclude the entry or exit of energy from the system and since energy is a conserved quantity, the total energy of the system must remain constant and we will designate this quantity by the symbol $U$. We now introduce a postulate which underlies the first law of thermodynamics. *For an adiabatically isolated system of given total energy U, given total volume V, and given compositional variables (mole numbers of constituents), there exists a unique equilibrium state which fixes the values of all other macroscopic parameters* (postulate based on empirical generalization). Thus for such a state the value of any other macroscopic parameter of interest, the temperature for instance, can be represented by

$$\theta = f(U, V, n_1, n_2, \ldots, n_r) \qquad (4\text{-}1)$$

Alternatively, we might note that the total energy of an equilibrium system is uniquely determined by the volume compositional variables and any one additional macroscopic variable, which we will for the moment choose to be temperature. It then follows that

$$U = U(V, \theta, n_1, n_2, \ldots, n_r) \qquad (4\text{-}2)$$

The right-hand side now consists of macroscopically measurable quantities and we turn our attention to the measurability of $U$.

First consider a system which is adiabatically isolated and has a certain set of values $V, \theta, n_1, n_2, \ldots, n_r$. Next permit a relaxation of the rigid-wall condition and allow external work to be done on the system by some arrangement of pistons, levers, pulleys, wheels, and other macroscopic devices. Now reisolate the system and allow it to equilibrate. A measured amount of mechanical work is done on the system. Since energy is conserved, we must argue that

$$\Delta U = \Delta W \qquad (4\text{-}3)$$

Thus the energy difference between the two particular states of the system can be measured. We next consider any two arbitrary equilibrium states of the system $A$ and $B$. If it were always possible to go from one state to another by external macroscopic mechanical work alone, then it would always be possible to measure the energy difference $\Delta U_{AB}$. In the previous statements we must envision the possibility of the system doing external work as well as the possibility of doing external work on the system.

In an elegant series of experiments carried out largely by William Prescott Joule it was in fact found *that given two equilibrium states of an isolated system A and B, it is always possible by external mechanical work alone to go either from state A to state B or from state B to state A* (empirical generalization). It is not always possible to go both ways by external mechanical work alone. This is related to the concept of reversibility and will be considered later. Joule's empirical generalization coupled with the previous postulate on total energy means that the total energy difference between any two equilibrium states is always measurable in terms of mechanical work or that the total energy $U$ is always measurable relative to some arbitrary zero level of energy. This arbitrary zero is a property of energy in mechanics and need not be of special concern to us in our thermal studies; we need only adopt some standard state and can then measure energy relative to that state.

The quantity $U$ is often designated internal energy rather than total energy of the system and this designation will be used in subsequent pages. We may now sum up the preceding ideas. For isolated systems at equilibrium there exists an internal energy which is a function of the macroscopic variables of the system. A corollary of being a function of the values of the macroscopic variables at equilibrium only is that the value of $U$ is independent of how the system arrived at its present state. The internal energy is a measurable quantity which ultimately relates thermodynamics to mechanics.

## B. THE FIRST LAW OF THERMODYNAMICS

The next problem is to investigate energy exchanges between the system and the environment by processes other than just the performance of external mechanical work. To allow for such exchange, we must relax the condition of adiabatic walls and allow energy exchanges by placing the system in contact with hotter or colder systems in the environment. To treat this process formally, we must reconsider the concept of equilibrium as introduced in Chapter III. Systems may achieve equilibrium either by adiabatic isolation or by being in contact with a very large isothermal reservoir. Consider a constant-volume system which has come to equilibrium with a large thermal reservoir. Such a system can be characterized by its macroscopic parameters $V, \theta, n_1, n_2, \ldots, n_r$. *If we now surround the system by adiabatic walls, the values of the macroscopic parameters will remain unchanged* (empirical generalization). The isolated systems will have an internal energy $U$ and some relation $U = U(V, \theta, n_1, n_2, \ldots, n_r)$ will obtain. Surrounding the system by adiabatic walls does not change its total energy, so that the value of $U$ and the relation between $U$ and $V$, $\theta$, $n_1$, $n_2$, ..., $n_r$ must be the same for the system before and after adiabatic isolation. The same equilibrium states exist under the two conditions of achieving equilibrium.

Next we consider a system in equilibrium state $A$ which interacts with the environment both by external mechanical work and by the flow of thermal energy. These interactions take the system to a new equilibrium state $B$. We can now write the following generalized statement of the conservation of energy:

$$U_B - U_A =\text{ energy exchanges of the system by external}$$
mechanical work $+$ energy exchanges of the system by all other processes

$$\Delta U = \Delta W + \Delta Q \tag{4-4}$$

We have already noted that $\Delta U$ is measurable and $\Delta W$ is available from a consideration of mechanics. Equation (4-4), which is called the first law of thermodynamics, serves to define $\Delta Q$, the heat flow or energy exchange of a system by all processes not subject to analysis by consideration of macroscopic mechanics. The functions $Q$ and $W$ have a different status from the function $U$ in that they depend not only on the state of the system but the path undergone in transitions of the system. Consider a simple example to clarify this point; an initial state consisting of $x$ grams of ice and $y$ grams of water at $0°C$ and a final state of $x + y$ grams of water at $25°C$. Consider two possible paths from the initial to the final state:

(a)   The system is adiabatically isolated, connected to the outside by a paddle wheel, which is turned by an external torque, the turning continuing until the system is at $25°C$.

(b)   The system is placed in contact with an isothermal reservoir at $25°C$ and is kept there until its temperature comes to $25°C$.

In both cases $\Delta U$ is the same since the same initial and final states are employed. In the first case, $\Delta W = \Delta U$ and $\Delta Q = 0$, while in the second case, $\Delta Q = \Delta U$ and $\Delta W = 0$. It is clear that $\Delta Q$ and $\Delta W$ are not functions of the state of the system, but depend on the path.

The first law of thermodynamics is thus seen as a generalized statement of the conservation of energy for systems involving thermal energy exchanges. The generalized conservation of energy is postulated and the heat term $\Delta Q$ is introduced as a bookkeeping device to maintain the balance of Equation (4-4). The unique aspect of the internal energy $U$ is that for equilibrium systems it is a function of state only and is independent of how the equilibrium state was reached.

Heat is not a form of energy, it is a method of energy flow. The only system property corresponding to heat is internal kinetic energy, but the exact distribution of energy between kinetic modes and potential energy within the system is a function of the detailed structure of the system and does not, at equilibrium, depend upon how energy enters the system. It is of course true that a system which has not reached equilibrium will be in a state which depends on its past history. The study of such systems, which may be very important for biology, is the subject matter of nonequilibrium thermodynamics, a field of study which is in its infancy and about which very little is known.

The equivalence of heat and mechanical work is indicated in Equation (4-4) and the preceding discussion requires a consideration of the units of measurement. The existence of separate heat and work units reflects in part the history of the subject insofar as there existed separate sciences of calorimetry and mechanics before the experiments of Joule and others established the first law of thermodynamics and the concept of the mechanical equivalent of heat. The heat unit chosen, the calorie (the name itself is a carry-over from the old caloric theory), is defined as the quantity of heat necessary to change the temperature of 1 gm of water from 3.5°C to 4.5°C. The large calorie or kilogram calorie is 1000 times the size of the calorie. The mean calorie is 1/100th of the quantity of heat necessary to raise the temperature of 1 gm of water from 0°C to 100°C. The older definition implies a change of state of 1 gm of water in equilibrium at 3.5°C and 1 atm pressure to equilibrium at 4.5°C and 1 atm. The change of state is carried out under conditions where $\Delta W = 0$. The heat flow is then one calorie (1 cal). We could carry out the same change of state under adiabatic conditions and find that $\Delta W = 4.185 \times 10^7$ ergs. A wide variety of experiments of this type have been completed and, as is implied from the first law, the relation between $\Delta W$ and $\Delta Q$ is a universal one, so that the quantity $4.185 \times 10^7$ ergs/cal is a universal constant designated as the mechanical equivalent of heat.

The calorie can in principle now be abandoned as a unit of measurement since we now have sufficient information to formulate all of thermodynamics in energy units. However, tradition dies hard and it appears that the calorie will be with us for some time to come.

PROBLEMS

1. Consider the following initial and final states and in each case
   discuss two alternate pathways to go from one state to the other
   (ideal gas scale temperatures are used in Problems 1 and 2):

   a. Two moles of hydrogen gas and two moles of oxygen gas at
      300° and 1 atm going to one mole of water at 300° and 1 atm.
   b. Solid carbon dioxide (dry ice) at 190° and 10 atm going to
      $CO_2$ gas at 1 atm and 300°.

2. In case 1(a), find the pathway that will result in the maximum
   amount of external work.

3. The energy from a falling 1-kg weight is used to heat water. If 50 gm
   of water is heated from 3°C to 90°C, how far must the weight fall?

# CHAPTER V

# The Second Law of Thermodynamics

*It must be admitted, I think, that the laws of
thermodynamics have a different feel from most
of the other laws of the physicist. There is something more palpably verbal about them—they
smell more of their human origin. The guiding
motif is strange to most of physics: namely, a
capitalizing of the universal failure of human
beings to construct perpetual motion machines of
either the first or the second kind. Why should
we expect nature to be interested either positively
or negatively in the purposes of human beings,
particularly purposes of such an unblushingly
economic tinge?*

P. W. BRIDGMAN

in " The Nature of Thermodynamics "

Harvard University Press, 1941

There are few ideas in science that have been as difficult to comprehend as the second law of thermodynamics and the accompanying
introduction of the entropy function. The concepts were originally
introduced in an engineering context, indeed Sadi Carnot's original
monograph was entitled " Reflections on the Motive Power of Fire and
on Machines Fitted to Develop that Power." From these considerations

of steam engines a series of concepts has arisen which have profoundly influenced physics, chemistry, and a number of related sciences, including biology. The recently discovered relationships between entropy, work, and information and the profoundly informational character of biology have served to stress the deep connections between biology and thermal physics.

In the following two chapters we introduce this subject in a traditional way. In order to really understand thermodynamics, it is necessary to comprehend how certain verbal statements about what cannot be done have been elaborated into some of our profoundest thoughts about the nature of the universe. In subsequent chapters we will then develop informational concepts which more closely relate entropic concepts to biology and allow us to sense the relation between the observer and the phenomena being observed.

## A. HEAT ENGINES AND REFRIGERATORS

The classical approach to thermodynamics starts with a consideration of heat engines and refrigerators. In the final analysis the theory is designed to deal with real engines and real refrigerators; however, in elaborating the theory, certain limiting idealizations are used. If we are careful to define our concepts, this difference between real and idealized engines and refrigerators will not be a cause of misunderstanding. The entities that we wish to deal with are then:

*a. Heat Engine. A heat engine is a device which takes heat from a hot source and performs mechanical work* (definition). The hot source can be the combustion of gasoline, the steam from a boiler, the heat of the sun or any other heat source. In order to continuously produce work, it is necessary for an engine to work in a cycle, that is, it must take in heat, produce work, and return to its original state so that it can repeat the process and continuously produce work. *It is found that if an engine does not operate in a cycle, its internal state changes until it reaches a point where it can no longer function* (empirical generalization). Our concern will then be with heat engines which operate in a cyclic fashion.

*b. Refrigerator. A refrigerator is a device which transfers heat from a cold body to a hotter body* (definition). Refrigerators which operate continuously also operate in cycles; that is, they must transfer heat and return to their original state so as to repeat the process. It is generally found that mechanical work must be performed in order to accomplish this kind of heat transfer.

## B. STATEMENTS OF THE SECOND LAW

The second law of thermodynamics was originally formulated in two different ways, one a statement about heat engines and the second a statement about refrigerators. In subsequent considerations it is necessary to use both statements interchangeably, so that we must prove their equivalence. These statements are the foundation upon which all of classical thermodynamics is based. Our procedure will be to state the two forms of the second law and then to prove their logical equivalence:

1.  Engine statement of the second law: *It is impossible to construct an engine that, operating in a cycle, will produce no effect other than the extraction of heat from a reservoir and the performance of an equivalent amount of work* (empirical generalization).
2.  Refrigerator statement of the second law: *It is impossible to construct a device that, operating in a cycle, will produce no effect other than the transfer of heat from a cooler to a hotter body* (empirical generalization).

To prove the logical equivalence of the two statements we will use formal symbolic logic, utilizing the following symbols:

*a.* Equivalence $\equiv$; $A \equiv B$; $A$ is logically equivalent to $B$.
*b.* Implication $\supset$; $A \supset B$; $A$ implies $B$, the truth of $A$ implies the truth of $B$.
*c.* Negation $-$; $-A$, which is read "not $A$"; either $A$ is true or $-A$ is true.

We now quote a result of formal logic which seems intuitively clear without formal proof. $A \equiv B$ if $A \supset B$ and $B \supset A$, that is, $A$ is equivalent to $B$ if the truth of $A$ implies the truth of $B$ and the truth of $B$ implies the truth of $A$. An alternative formulation of equivalence is $A \equiv B$ if $-A \supset -B$ and $-B \supset -A$, that is, $A$ is equivalent to $B$ if the falsity of $A$ implies the falsity of $B$ and the falsity of $B$ implies the falsity of $A$. We shall use the second form of proving equivalence; that is, we may assume that the engine statement of the second law is logically equivalent to the refrigerator statement of the second law if the falsity of the engine statement implies the falsity of the refrigerator statement and the falsity of the refrigerator statement implies the falsity of the engine statement.

The engine statement specifically rules out an engine that can extract energy from a heat source and convert it to work with no other effects. The classical example of such an engine would be one that could extract heat energy from the ocean and drive an ocean liner without the necessity of buying fuel. What in fact happens is that actual engines not only take heat from a hot reservoir but give up heat to a cold reservoir.

We now assume the falsity of the refrigerator statement and consider the device shown in Figure 5-1. The engine operates by taking up an amount of heat $Q$ from the hot reservoir, doing an amount of work $W$, and giving up an amount of heat $Q - W$ to the cold reservoir. If the refrigerator could violate the refrigerator statement of the second law, it could transfer an amount of heat $Q - W$ from the cold to the hot reservoir. The engine and refrigerator working together would then take up an amount of heat $W$ from the hot reservoir and do an amount of work $W$ and produce no other effect. The whole device would then violate the engine statement of the second law. Therefore the assumed falsity of the refrigerator statement implies the falsity of the engine statement.

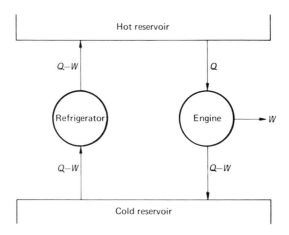

**Fig. 5-1.** An engine and a refrigerator working between two reservoirs at different temperatures. The engine takes in an amount of heat $Q$, does an amount of work $W$, and rejects an amount of heat $Q - W$. The refrigerator (acting contrary to the refrigerator statement of the second law) transfers an amount of heat $Q - W$ from the cold reservoir to the hot reservoir.

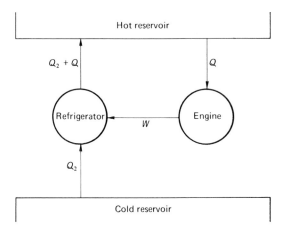

**Fig. 5-2.** An engine and a refrigerator working between two reservoirs at different temperatures. The engine (in violation of the engine statement of the second law) takes in an amount of heat $Q$ and does an equivalent amount of work $W$. The work is done on a refrigerator which then takes up an amount of heat $Q_2$ from the cold reservoir and transfers an amount of heat $Q_2 + W$, which is $Q_2 + Q$, to the hot reservoir.

Next assume the falsity of the engine statement of the second law. Referring to Figure 5-2, the engine would now take up an amount of energy $Q$ and do an amount of work $W = Q$. This work could be used to drive a refrigerator which would take up an amount of heat $Q_2$ and transfer $Q_2 + Q$ to the hot reservoir. The entire device of engine and refrigerator now acts cyclically to cause no other effect than the transfer of $Q_2$ units from the cold reservoir to the hot reservoir, which violates the refrigerator statement of the second law.

If we designate the engine statement as $E$ and the refrigerator statement as $R$, we have now demonstrated that

$$-E \supset -R \qquad \text{and} \qquad -R \supset -E$$

which implies that $R \equiv E$. The two statements of the second law are logically equivalent and can be used interchangeably.


## C. CARNOT CYCLES

The second law can now be used to derive two important theorems, known as Carnot's theorems, about the efficiency of engines. These theorems can in turn be used to develop an absolute thermodynamic temperature scale. We shall then be able to show the complete equivalence of this scale with the perfect-gas temperature scale. This should then complete our formalization of the concept of temperature.

Three notions are required prior to our statement and proof of Carnot's theorems. These are the definition of efficiency, the detailing of the concept of reversibility, and the introduction of the Carnot cycle or ideal reversible engine.

a. *Efficiency. The efficiency of a heat engine is the ratio of the mechanical work produced to the heat taken in from the hot source* (definition). This may be formally stated as

$$\eta = \frac{W}{Q_1} \tag{5-1}$$

where $W$ is work and $Q_1$ is the heat taken in. As we have already noted an engine also gives up heat to a cold reservoir in completing its cycle. If we designate this amount of heat as $Q_2$, we can then utilize the first law of thermodynamics to write

$$\Delta U = Q_1 - W - Q_2 \tag{5-2}$$

For a complete cycle the engine returns to its original state and $\Delta U = 0$ since we have already noted that $U$ is a function of the state of the system only. Equation (5-2) can then be rewritten as

$$W = Q_1 - Q_2 \tag{5-3}$$

and the efficiency can be formulated as

$$\eta = \frac{W}{Q_1} = \frac{Q_1 - Q_2}{Q_1} = 1 - \frac{Q_2}{Q_1} \tag{5-4}$$

The engine form of the statement of the second law is equivalent to saying that $\eta$ must always be less than one, all heat engines must have efficiencies less than unity.

b. *Reversibility.* Consider a simple one-component system which is originally at an equilibrium state characterized by $P_1$ and $\theta_1$ and which under the influence of external changes moves to another equilibrium state characterized by $P_2$, $\theta_2$. For simplicity allow the system to be in a cylinder whose pressure is maintained by an external piston and whose temperature is maintained by contact with an external heat reservoir as in Figure 5-3. Consider the following pathway from $P_1$, $\theta_1$ to $P_2$, $\theta_2$. First change the pressure by a tiny amount $\Delta P$ and allow the system to

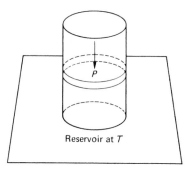

**Fig. 5-3.** Cylinder containing a one component system which is in contact with a reservoir at temperature *T*. An external piston allows the pressure to be brought to any value *P*.

reequilibrate. After it has equilibrated change the pressure by another tiny increment $\Delta P$ and again wait for equilibrium. Repeat this process until the system is at $P_2$. Next place the cylinder in contact with a reservoir at temperature $\theta + \Delta\theta$ and allow it to equilibrate. After equilibration place the cylinder in contact with a reservoir at temperature $\theta + 2\Delta\theta$ and again let the system come to an equilibrium state. Continue this process until the system comes to temperature $\theta_2$.

The process we have just described takes the system from state 1 to state 2 through an intermediate series of states all of which are equilibrium states. In fact, this is not quite true since every time we change the external conditions we must introduce transients and until these transients die out the system is not in equilibrium. However, if we make each $\Delta P$ and $\Delta\theta$ sufficiently small and if we carry out the process sufficiently slowly, then the system can be maintained arbitrarily close to equilibrium. Such slow small transformations are called quasistatic changes in the system. The changes are also called reversible, since at any point reversing the succession of $\Delta P$'s and $\Delta\theta$'s with $-\Delta P$'s and $-\Delta\theta$'s will reverse the succession of equilibrium states.

Returning to our previous example, we could have gone from state 1 to state 2 by changing the piston pressure suddenly from $P_1$ to $P_2$ and simultaneously placing the cylinder in contact with a reservoir at temperature $\theta_2$. The system will eventually equilibrate at the new boundary conditions $P_2$, $\theta_2$, but the intermediate states will involve pressure transients, thermal gradients, and other nonhomogeneous phenomenon, so that it will be impossible to describe the intervening states by a small number of parameters such as $P$ and $\theta$. In such a case it will be impossible to retrace the pathway and the transformation is designated an irreversible process. All real processes are irreversible, reversible changes being a limiting state. The idealization of reversibility is nevertheless an extremely important abstraction for equilibrium thermodynamics and it is critically important to the continued development of the subject. Consider Figure 5-4, which represents a $P$–$\theta$

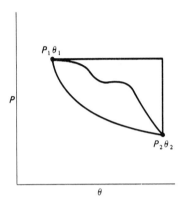

**Fig. 5-4.** Various pathways from the state $P_1\theta_1$ to the state $P_2\theta_2$.

diagram. Any path that can be represented on this diagram must be reversible, since points of well-defined $P$ and $\theta$ required to be represented on the graph are of necessity equilibrium points. The quantities $P$ and $\theta$ are only meaningful for the whole system when they are uniform throughout, which implies that the system is in equilibrium.

In general, any processes which involve friction or the local generation of heat will be irreversible since the reverse pathway would involve converting all this heat back to work, which violates the engine statement of the second law. The conditions for reversibility are that a process takes place quasistatically so as to always be arbitrarily near to equilibrium and that the process is not accompanied by any frictional effects.

*c. Carnot engines.* The concept of a Carnot engine arose out of an attempt to ask the question as to what is the maximum efficiency that can be obtained from an engine working in a cycle between a heat source at temperature $\theta_1$ and a heat sink at temperature $\theta_2$. The characteristics of such an engine are that it must take up a certain amount of heat $Q_1$ from the hot reservoir, perform a certain amount of work $W$, give up a certain amount of heat $Q_2$ to the cold reservoir, and return to the initial state. We will further require that the engine be reversible in the sense we have just discussed. The significance of reversibility for such an engine is that if it is operated in reverse it becomes a refrigerator on which an amount of work $W$ is done, accompanied by an amount of heat $Q_2$ being taken from the cold reservoir and $Q_1 = W + Q_2$ units of heat given up at the hot reservoir. This ability to retrace the path with the opposite external heat and work transfers is a fundamental feature of reversibility.

## D. CARNOT THEOREMS

Having introduced the previous series of concepts, we are now in a position to prove two very general theorems about heat engines.

*Theorem I.* No engine operating between two heat reservoirs can be more efficient than a reversible engine operating between the same two reservoirs.

*Proof:* We shall assume the existence of an engine more efficient than a reversible engine and show that it leads to a contradiction (Fig. 5-5):

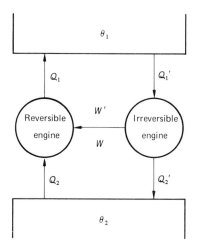

**Fig. 5-5.** An irreversible and reversible engine working between the same two heat reservoirs. The irreversible engine drives the reversible engine backward as a refrigerator.

|                                   | Reversible engine | Other engine |
|-----------------------------------|:-----------------:|:------------:|
| Heat taken up per cycle           | $Q_1$             | $Q_1'$       |
| Work done                         | $W$               | $W'$         |
| Heat given up to the cold reservoir | $Q_2$           | $Q_2'$       |
| Efficiency                        | $\eta = \dfrac{W}{Q_1}$ | $\eta' = \dfrac{W'}{Q_1'}$ |
| Assume $\eta' > \eta$             |                   |              |

Working between the same two reservoirs at $\theta_1$ and $\theta_2$, we will allow the irreversible engine to operate the reversible engine backward as a refrigerator, and in that case, $W = W'$, all the work output of the engine is used to drive the refrigerator. The two devices working together therefore do no net work but transfer an amount of heat $Q_1 - Q_1' = Q_2 - Q_2'$ between the reservoirs.

From the assumed efficiencies

$$\eta' = \frac{W'}{Q_1'} > \frac{W}{Q_1} = \eta \tag{5-5}$$

Since $W = W'$,

$$\frac{1}{Q_1'} > \frac{1}{Q_1}, \qquad Q_1 > Q_1' \tag{5-6}$$

The quantity $Q_1 - Q_1'$ is therefore positive. But this is the heat transferred to the hot reservoir. The two engines acting together in a cycle would thus transfer heat from the cold reservoir to the hot reservoir. This, however, is contrary to the refrigerator statement of the second law, hence $\eta'$ is not greater than $\eta$, which may be formally stated as

$$\eta \geq \eta' \tag{5-7}$$

*Theorem II.* All reversible engines operating between the same two temperatures have the same efficiency.

The proof of this theorem is a simple extension of the proof of the last theorem. We designate the two engines as $a$ and $b$. We first assume $\eta_a > \eta_b$ and show it leads to a contradiction. We then assume $\eta_b > \eta_a$ and show that this leads to a contradiction. The only remaining possibility is that $\eta_a = \eta_b$. We proceed by allowing engine $b$ to drive engine $a$ backward as a refrigerator.

|                  | Engine $a$ | Engine $b$ |
|------------------|------------|------------|
| Heat taken in    | $Q_{a1}$   | $Q_{b1}$   |
| Work done        | $W_a$      | $W_b$      |
| Heat discharged  | $Q_{a2}$   | $Q_{b2}$   |

Assume

$$\eta_b > \eta_a \tag{5-8}$$

Then

$$\frac{W_b}{Q_{b1}} > \frac{W_a}{Q_{a1}}, \qquad W_a = W_b, \qquad Q_{a1} > Q_{b1} \tag{5-9}$$

The net effect of the two engines is to transfer an amount of heat $Q_{a1} - Q_{b1}$ from the cold reservoir to the hot reservoir, which is a violation of the second law of thermodynamics; hence

$$\eta_b \leqslant \eta_a \tag{5-10}$$

By reversing the procedure and allowing engine $a$ to drive engine $b$ as a refrigerator, we can show

$$\eta_b \geqslant \eta_a \tag{5-11}$$

The only way of simultaneously satisfying both equations is to assume

$$\eta_b = \eta_a \tag{5-12}$$

The efficiency of a reversible engine is thus independent of the working substance and independent of the exact mode of operation of the engine; it appears to depend only on the temperatures of the two reservoirs. This dependence of the efficiency on the temperature and the independence on the details of the engine suggests that efficiency might provide an absolute measure of temperature independent of the detailed nature of the thermometer.

## E. The Thermodynamic Temperature Scale

To develop this concept of temperature, consider that the temperatures of the two reservoirs are measured on an empirical temperature scale and found to be $\theta_1$ and $\theta_2$. From our previous discussion the efficiency of a reversible engine operating between these two reservoirs is thus a function of $\theta_1$ and $\theta_2$:

$$\eta_{12} = \Phi(\theta_1, \theta_2) = 1 - \frac{Q_2}{Q_1} \tag{5-13}$$

The ratio of $Q_2$ to $Q_1$ is therefore also a function of $\theta_1$ and $\theta_2$, which we can designate as $\Theta(\theta_1, \theta_2)$.

We now consider three engines, one operating between $\theta_1$, and $\theta_2$, as we have just discussed, and the other two operating between $\theta_3$ as the hot reservoir and $\theta_1$ and $\theta_2$ as the cold reservoirs. We can then write

$$\frac{Q_2}{Q_1} = \Theta(\theta_1, \theta_2), \qquad \frac{Q_1}{Q_3} = \Theta(\theta_3, \theta_1), \qquad \frac{Q_2}{Q_3} = \Theta(\theta_3, \theta_2) \tag{5-14}$$

The three equations can be combined in a simple way to yield

$$\frac{Q_2}{Q_1} = \frac{Q_2/Q_3}{Q_1/Q_3} = \frac{\Theta(\theta_3, \theta_2)}{\Theta(\theta_3, \theta_1)} = \Theta(\theta_1, \theta_2) \tag{5-15}$$

The right-hand equality of Equation (5-15) places certain mathematical restrictions on the function $\Theta$. In general, the requirement is that $\Theta(\theta_i, \theta_j)$ is equal to the product of two functions, one of $\theta_i$ and the other of $\theta_j$. Thus $\Theta(\theta_i, \theta_j)$ must be of the form $A(\theta_i)B(\theta_j)$. If we apply this condition to Equation (5-15), we get

$$\frac{Q_2}{Q_1} = \frac{A(\theta_2)B(\theta_3)}{A(\theta_1)B(\theta_3)} = \frac{A(\theta_2)}{A(\theta_1)} \tag{5-16}$$

The Kelvin absolute thermodynamic temperature $T$ will then be defined by the following relation:

$$\frac{T_1}{T_2} = \frac{Q_1}{Q_2} = \frac{A(\theta_1)}{A(\theta_2)} \tag{5-17}$$

The absolute values of $T$ are established by assigning as the temperature of the triple point of water $T = 273.16°$. The temperature scale so defined has the following properties:

1.  It is independent of the working substance of the thermometer (the engine) because of Carnot's second theorem.
2.  It has an absolute zero since

$$\eta = 1 - \frac{T_2}{T_1} \leqslant 1 \tag{5-18}$$

The inequality is a result of the first law of thermodynamics, since an engine cannot put out more work than its input of heat. Since

$$T_2 \geqslant 0 \tag{5-19}$$

there cannot be sinks with a negative value of $T_2$, and there is a lowest possible value of $T_2$, which is zero.

3. It is a very inconvenient thermometer to use because measuring the efficiency of a perfect reversible engine is a very difficult feat to perform experimentally.

In order to overcome the difficulty in actually using the Kelvin absolute thermodynamic temperature, we investigate the relation between the scale and a specific empirical temperature scale, that of the perfect-gas thermometer. When this is done we are able to show that the absolute thermodynamic temperature is exactly equal to the perfect-gas empirical temperature. We are thus provided with an experimental method for the measurement of absolute temperature and we are able to tie together all of our various temperature concepts.

The general proof of the equivalence of the two temperature scales, while simple and straightforward, is rather laborious. We will proceed by outlining the method of proof in the following few lines and presenting the detailed proof in Appendix II. The proof proceeds by constructing an engine from an ideal gas, calculating the efficiency of the engine based on the equations of state of the gas, and determining the quantity

$$\frac{Q_1}{Q_2} = \frac{A(\theta_1)}{A(\theta_2)} \tag{5-20}$$

In actually carrying out the detailed calculation, we arrive at the result

$$\frac{A(\theta_1)}{A(\theta_2)} = \frac{\theta_1}{\theta_2} \tag{5-21}$$

We are therefore able to show, by combining the results of Equations (5-17) and (5-21), that

$$\frac{\theta_1}{\theta_2} = \frac{T_1}{T_2} \tag{5-22}$$

Choosing the reference temperature for both scales as the critical point of water at 273.16° completes the identity of the two scales. What we therefore require is the formal proof of Equation (5-21), which may be found in Appendix II.

From Equation (5-22) we are able to conclude that perfect-gas temperature and absolute thermodynamic temperature are proportional. If we pick the same fixed point for each scale (the critical point of water), then perfect-gas temperature and absolute thermodynamic temperature are identical.

We now have a temperature scale with the following properties:

1. It is independent of the working substance.
2. It has a natural zero.
3. It is measurable with an empirical thermometer that can be used as a primary standard.

Three separate temperature notions have been introduced: (a) empirical temperature; (b) kinetic theory temperature; (c) absolute thermodynamic temperature. These three temperatures have been shown in the case of the ideal gas to be identical. Much of the power of thermal physics comes from being able to work back and forth within a conceptual framework which stresses varied aspects of a given problem.

PROBLEMS

1. The refrigerator statement of the second law of thermodynamics has been interpreted as meaning that the universe is running down-hill and consequently must have a finite age. Explain this interpretation.

2. In the operation of a muscle there appears to be a direct conversion of chemical potential energy into mechanical work. Compare such an engine with a heat engine and comment on the maximum possible efficiency.

3. Explain why the growth of a cell to yield two daughter cells is an irreversible process.

# CHAPTER VI

# The Entropy Function

*A good many times I have been present at gatherings of people who by standards of the traditional culture are thought highly educated and who have with considerable gusto been expressing their incredulity at the illiteracy of scientists. Once or twice I have been provoked and have asked the company how many of them could describe the Second Law of Thermodynamics. The response was cold: it was also negative. Yet I was asking something which is about the scientific equivalent of : Have you read a work of Shakespeare's?*

" The Two Cultures and the Scientific Revolution"
by C. P. Snow
Cambridge University Press, 1959

## A. STATE FUNCTIONS

The entropy function has been an enigma to students of thermodynamics since its introduction many years ago. Originally introduced to provide a function of state related to the heat flow $dQ$, it was soon discovered to provide the most general and succinct statement of the condition of equilibrium in any equilibrium system. With the introduction of kinetic theory, entropy, through the Boltzmann $H$-theorem, provided the most general notion of mechanical irreversibility. The development of statistical mechanics used entropy to bridge the gap between the statistical formalism and phenomenological thermodynamics. Finally the modern notions of information relates entropy to information and ultimately to the observer. All of these considerations make the notion of entropy central to biology and provides strong incentive to penetrate the conceptual difficulties.

Before discussing entropy per se we will briefly review the mathematics of a function of two variables $f(x, y)$. Such a function is a function of state in that its value depends only on the values of the independent parameters of the system $x$ and $y$ and is independent of the path taken to arrive at the state $x$ and $y$. The differential of such a function can be written

$$df = \frac{\partial f}{\partial x} dx + \frac{\partial f}{\partial y} dy \tag{6-1}$$

$$df = M(x, y)\, dx + N(x, y)\, dy \tag{6-2}$$

A path between $x_1, y_1$ and $x_2, y_2$ can be represented by a relation

$$\Omega(x, y) = 0 \tag{6-3}$$

where $\Omega$ is some function of $x$ and $y$ plus constants. For instance, if the path is a straight line, $\Omega(x, y)$ is of the form $y - mx - b$. Since $f$ is a state function, Equation (6-1) can be integrated directly,

$$\int_{x_1 y_1}^{x_2 y_2} df = f(x_2, y_2) - f(x_1, y_1) \tag{6-4}$$

The integral must be independent of the path since it depends only on the values of the function at the termini of the paths. A direct consequence of (6-1) and (6-2) and the theory of partial differentials is that

$$\frac{\partial M}{\partial y} = \frac{\partial^2 f}{\partial x\, \partial y} = \frac{\partial N}{\partial x} \tag{6-5}$$

Many of the most important relations of thermodynamics are derived by the use of Equation (6-5). Assume we now integrate $df$ over a closed path beginning and ending at $x_1, y_1$:

$$\oint df = \int_{x_1 y_1}^{x_1 y_1} df = f(x_1, y_1) - f(x_1, y_1) = 0 \tag{6-6}$$

The property of having the line integral vanish is a characteristic feature of state functions and may be used to identify a state function. The vanishing of the line integral is equivalent to the function being a function of state only. Refer to Figure 6-1 and consider some arbitrary

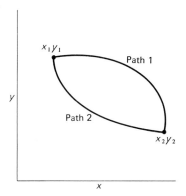

**Fig. 6-1.** Two possible paths of integration from the point $x_1 y_1$ to the point $x_2 y_2$.

point $x_2, y_2$ on the closed path. The vanishing of the line integral implies the following equation, since the total line integral can be divided into a series of successive integrals:

$$\oint df = \int_{x_1 y_1}^{x_2 y_2} df + \int_{x_2 y_2}^{x_1 y_1} df = 0 \qquad (6\text{-}7)$$

By a straightforward transformation of the limits, Equation (6-7) can be rewritten as

$$\int_{x_1 y_1}^{x_2 y_2} df - \int_{x_1 y_1}^{x_2 y_2} df = 0 \qquad (6\text{-}8)$$

The first term is the integral from $x_1, y_1$ to $x_2, y_2$ by path 1, while the second term is the integral from $x_1, y_1$ to $x_2, y_2$ by path 2. We may rewrite this equation in the following form:

$$\int_{\substack{x_1 y_1 \\ \text{path 1}}}^{x_2 y_2} df = \int_{\substack{x_1 y_1 \\ \text{path 2}}}^{x_2 y_2} df \qquad (6\text{-}9)$$

The vanishing of the line integral is thus equivalent to the integral being independent of the path. This rather abstract mathematical point has been labored because we shall shortly use the vanishing of the line integral to show that entropy is a state function.

## B. INTEGRALS OF $dQ$

We have already shown that $U$ is a function of state while $Q$ and $W$ are not. Recalling the first law for a simple one-component system, we see that

$$dU = dQ - P\, dV \qquad (6\text{-}10)$$

While $dW$ is not an exact differential, it is the product of a state variable $P$ and an exact differential $dV$ (change of volume). The question arose early in the development of the theory, "Could $dQ$ be represented in terms of state variables and exact differentials?" If this were possible, it would imply important mathematical advantages in dealing with Equation (6-10). Our method of approaching the problem is to employ the operation of optimism; that is, we assume that we can represent $dQ$ as the product of some function of state variables times an exact differential and proceed to find the properties of the relevant quantities. We assume that

$$dQ = (\text{function of state})\; x\; dS \qquad (6\text{-}11)$$

where $dS$ is an exact differential. If we can find appropriate functions, then our optimism is justified and we can use the new function $S$. $S$ is called the entropy and we must now prove that it exists and has the requisite properties. While this may seem a curious method of approach, it has two virtues: first, it works, and second, it can ultimately be justified by very sophisticated and rigorous methods of analysis. While we shall not be able to present the exacting Principle of Caratheodory, we should be aware of its existence and of the fact that it provides a rigorous conceptual foundation for the material we are discussing.*

If we assume Equation (6-11), we can write $dU$ as

$$dU = \left(\frac{\partial U}{\partial S}\right)_V dS + \left(\frac{\partial U}{\partial V}\right)_S dV \qquad (6\text{-}12)$$

---

* A discussion of the Principle of Caratheodory is found in *The Mathematics of Physics and Chemistry* by H. Margenau and G. M. Murphy, D. Van Nostrand Co., 1943.

We have the following requirements to satisfy in order for Equations (6-10) and (6-12) to be in agreement:

$$\left(\frac{\partial U}{\partial V}\right)_S = -P \tag{6-13}$$

$$\left(\frac{\partial U}{\partial S}\right)_V dS = dQ \tag{6-14}$$

We still have considerable arbitrariness left in the choice of the function $S$ and we narrow down that choice by trying to establish the functions so that $T$ plays a role analogous to $-P$ in Equations (6-10) and (6-12). This then would require

$$\left(\frac{\partial U}{\partial S}\right)_V = T \tag{6-15}$$

Equations (6-12)–(6-15) would lead to the following expression for the entropy:

$$dS = \frac{dU + P\,dV}{T} = \frac{dQ}{T} \tag{6-16}$$

We may regard Equation (6-16) as the defining equation for a function $S$ which satisfies conditions (6-14) and (6-15). Proof that $S$ is a state function then would complete the problem and allow us to use the results for subsequent analysis.

## C. PROPERTIES OF THE ENTROPY FUNCTION

For perfect gases we know $U$ as a function of $T$ and we have a relation between $P$, $V$, and $T$, so that we can substitute directly into Equation (6-16), obtain the entropy function, and show that it has all the desired properties. This is done in Appendix III.

In the more general case we do not have $U$ as a function of the state variables, so we take a less direct approach. The proof we shall offer is not completely rigorous, but is intuitively satisfactory. The rigorous approach, as we have pointed out, involves a degree of mathematical sophistication that goes beyond what we shall attempt in this book, so, for the moment, we may satisfy ourselves with the knowledge that a rigorous proof does exist.

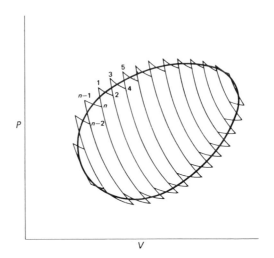

**Fig. 6-2.** An arbitrary closed loop in $PV$ space is divided up into a number of Carnot cycles whose envelope approaches arbitrarily close to the initial curve. The path of integration is from 1 to 2 to 3 to 4 to ... $n-1$ to $n$ to 1.

$S$ will be shown to be a state function by demonstrating that $\oint dS = 0$. Consider an arbitrary closed curve in $P$–$V$ space (Figure 6-2). Divide the area up into a large number of Carnot cycles. For each Carnot cycle

$$\frac{q_1}{T_1} = \frac{q_2}{T_2} \quad \text{or} \quad \frac{q_1}{T_1} - \frac{q_2}{T_2} = 0$$

Allowing the plus or minus sign to be part of the $q$, we get

$$\frac{q_1}{T_1} + \frac{q_2}{T_2} = 0$$

Instead of integrating $dS$ along the actual curve, we integrate along the Carnot cycles approaching the curve. Along the adiabatics, $q = 0$.

Along the isothermals, the $q$'s always appear pairwise, so that their sum divided by $T$ is zero. Therefore along the Carnot cycle curves $\oint dS = 0$. Since these curves can arbitrarily approach the actual curve by taking more and more cycles within the area, we conclude that $\oint dS = 0$ for the actual curve. The entropy $S$ is thus a function of state. Therefore entropy is a property of an equilibrium system. It is not easy to convey a physically intuitive notion of this property in the sense that temperature and volume correspond to abstractions from direct experience. It is perhaps instructive to consider the analogy between the $P\,dV$ and $T\,dS$ terms. In doing work, pressure is the driving force and volume is the extensive property of the system that changes. We could of course write $dV = -dW/P$. Similarly, in heat flow, temperature is the driving force and entropy is the extensive property of the system that changes. Entropy has the units of energy divided by temperature.

Since entropy is a state function, relations can be formulated between entropy and other state variables as indicated below:

$$S = S(P, V) = S(P, T) = S(V, T) = S(P, U) = S(U, T) \quad (6\text{-}17)$$

Next consider the relationship between entropy and the refrigerator statement of the second law of thermodynamics. If we transfer heat $dQ$ from a colder body at temperature $T_2$ to a hotter body at temperature $T_1$, the total entropy change is

$$dS = -\frac{dQ}{T_2} + \frac{dQ}{T_1} = dQ\,\frac{(T_2 - T_1)}{T_1 T_2} \quad (6\text{-}18)$$

since $T_1 > T_2$,

$$dS < 0 \quad (6\text{-}19)$$

But this heat transfer is contrary to the refrigerator statement of the second law, which therefore requires in cases involving only heat flow that

$$dS \geqslant 0 \quad (6\text{-}20)$$

It turns out that the increase of entropy accompanying all real processes is an alternative and very general statement of the second law of thermodynamics.

Let us next consider the entropy changes accompanying the operation of real engines. First recall that for an ideal engine

$$\frac{Q_1}{T_1} = \frac{Q_2}{T_2} \quad (6\text{-}21)$$

The entropy change in one cycle is the sum of the entropy changes of the engine and the reservoir. Since the engine returns to its original state, its entropy change is zero. The net entropy change is that of the reservoirs, and that is:

$$\Delta S = -\frac{Q_1}{T_1} + \frac{Q_2}{T_2} = 0 \quad (6\text{-}22)$$

The zero sum in Equation 6-22 follows from Equation 6-21. For a real engine the efficiency is less than for an ideal reversible engine. Designating the heat taken in and discharged by a real engine as $Q_1'$ and $Q_2'$, we have as an expression of the efficiency

$$\eta' = 1 - \frac{Q_2'}{Q_1'} \tag{6-23}$$

However, Carnot's theorem requires that the efficiency of a real engine be less than that of an ideal reversible engine, which we have shown is $1 - (T_2/T_1)$. Consequently,

$$1 - \frac{Q_2'}{Q_1'} < 1 - \frac{T_2}{T_1} \tag{6-24}$$

If we rearrange the terms in Equation (6-24), we get

$$\frac{Q_2'}{T_2} > \frac{Q_1'}{T_1} \tag{6-25}$$

Consequently, the entropy change accompanying a cycle of a real engine is

$$\Delta S = -\frac{Q_1'}{T_1} + \frac{Q_2'}{T_2} > 0 \tag{6-26}$$

The operation of a real engine is accompanied by an entropy increase. Reexamining Equation (6-18), we can see that, if $T_2$ were greater than $T_1$, the entropy would increase. But since it is always observed that heat flows from a hot body to a cold body, heat flow is always accompanied by an entropy increase.

A somewhat different view of entropy comes from a consideration of the entropy of mixing of two gases. Consider two chambers, one of volume $V_A$ containing $n_A$ moles of perfect gas $A$ and the second of volume $V_B$ containing $n_B$ moles of perfect gas $B$ with the volumes chosen so that $P_A = P_B$ as in Figure 6-3. If we adiabatically isolate the

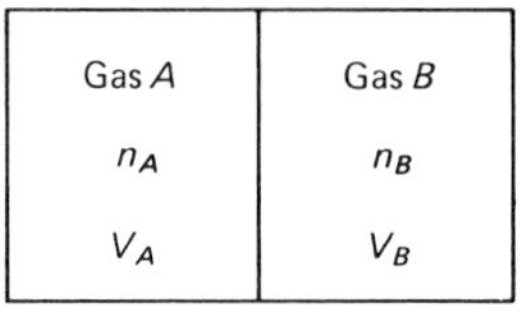

| Gas A | Gas B |
|-------|-------|
| $n_A$ | $n_B$ |
| $V_A$ | $V_B$ |

**Fig. 6-3.** Two compartments containing different gases. The pressures are equal in the two compartments.

system and open a hole between the two chambers, the gases will mix. There will be no external work and $\Delta Q$ will be zero; $U$ will remain unchanged and, accordingly, since $U$ is a function of $T$ only, $T$ will remain unchanged. The mixing of the two gases under these conditions is clearly an irreversible process.

We next consider a reversible path from the same initial to the same final state. To do this, we introduce another idealization, the concept of *a perfect selective membrane which will be impermeable to one species of molecule and will freely pass the other species* (definition). Such membranes can be approached experimentally, and indeed the phenomenon of osmosis, which we treat in Chapter XII, depends on the existence of such structures. We will utilize two idealized rigid, selective membranes (Figure 6-4), the first freely permeable to $A$ molecules but

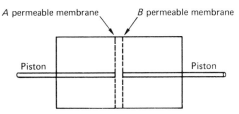

**Fig. 6-4.** The same chamber shown in Figure 6-3. The barrier is replaced by two membranes attached to pistons. One membrane is permeable only to $A$ molecules and the second permeable only to $B$ molecules.

impermeable to $B$ molecules, the second freely permeable to $B$ molecules but impermeable to $A$ molecules. Replace the center barrier by the two membranes, the $A$-permeable one to the left of the $B$-permeable one. Since both membranes are rigid, connect them to external pistons. Connect the whole system to an isothermal reservoir at temperature $T$ and allow the right-hand piston to move to the right reversibly to the edge of the chamber. Gas $A$ exerts a pressure $P_A$ on the membrane and gas $B$ exerts no pressure, since the membrane is freely permeable to $B$. The amount of work done is

$$W_A = \int_{V_A}^{V} P \, dV = \int_{V_A}^{V} \frac{n_A RT}{V} \, dV = RTn_A \ln \frac{V}{V_A} \qquad (6\text{-}27)$$

where $V = V_A + V_B$. Similarly, the amount of work necessary to bring the left-hand piston to the edge of the chamber is

$$W_B = RTn_B \ln \frac{V}{V_B} \qquad (6\text{-}28)$$

Since the final state is the same as in the previous case, we get

$$\Delta U = \Delta Q - \left( R T n_a \ln \frac{V}{V_A} + R T n_B \ln \frac{V}{V_B} \right) = 0 \qquad (6\text{-}29)$$

We rearrange terms in Equation (6-29), solve for $\Delta Q$, and compute $\Delta S$, which is simply $\Delta Q / T$ (since the process is isothermal),

$$\Delta S = R \left( n_A \ln \frac{V}{V_A} + n_B \ln \frac{V}{V_B} \right) \qquad (6\text{-}30)$$

In the irreversible mixing, $\Delta Q = 0$; hence

$$\Delta S_{\text{reversible}} > \int \frac{dQ}{T} \qquad (6\text{-}31)$$
$$\text{\scriptsize irreversible}$$

Formula (6-31) turns out to be of considerably more general validity than the single case just given and will get further attention later. Formula (6-30) is usually written in the form

$$\Delta S = -R \left( n_A \ln \frac{n_A}{n_A + n_B} + n_B \ln \frac{n_B}{n_A + n_B} \right) \qquad (6\text{-}32)$$

Note that, if molecules $A$ and $B$ were identical, it would have been impossible to have a membrane that could select between them. Consequently, the distinguishability of the molecules makes it possible to get the work $W_A + W_B$ out of the system. Mixing the molecules lowers this potential to do work and causes an entropy rise in the system.

In a very general way, entropy measures the orderliness of a system. Spontaneous processes tend toward equilibrium, which is the state of maximum disorder consistent with the constraints of the system. This state of maximum disorder is also the state of maximum entropy, a concept which will later become clearer in the discussions of entropy from a statistical-mechanical and informational point of view.

The global statement of the second law of thermodynamics may now be stated as follows:

    *a.*  There exists a function of state, the entropy, which is defined for reversible transformations by $dS = dQ/T$.

    *b.*  In all reversible transformations the entropy change of the universe (system plus reservoirs) remains constant.

    *c.*  All irreversible processes are accompanied by an increase of entropy.

d. The last two statements indicate that total entropy remains constant or increases but never decreases.

e. The equilibrium state is the state of maximum entropy of the system plus the surroundings. This is the most general condition of equilibrium.

Part *a* has already been demonstrated. Part *b* can be demonstrated in the following way. In reversible transformations, the entropy term always involves transfer of heat between a system and reservoir, so that

$$dS = dS_{system} + dS_{reservoir}$$

Since heat is transferred, $dQ_{system} = -dQ_{reservoir}$ and since the process is reversible, system and reservoir must be at approximately the same temperature, $T_{system} - T_{reservoir} = dT$; thus

$$dS = -\frac{dQ}{T + dT} + \frac{dQ}{T} = \frac{dQ\ dT}{T^2} \cong 0 \qquad (6\text{-}33)$$

Thus $dS$ is the product of two differentials and is consequently vanishingly small, particularly since the more nearly the process approaches reversibility, the more nearly does $dT$ approach zero.

Part *c* can be demonstrated by considering a system which undergoes an irreversible adiabatic process from equilibrium state *a* to equilibrium state *b*. We shall assume an entropy decrease and show that it leads to a violation of the second law of thermodynamics. Assume that $S_a > S_b$. We now return the system from state *b* to state *a* along some reversible path. Along this path

$$S_a - S_b = \int_{b\,\text{reversible}}^{a} \frac{dQ}{T} > 0 \qquad (6\text{-}34)$$

This condition is necessary since, by assumption, $S_a - S_b$ is positive. There must therefore be a flow of heat from reservoirs into the system. Since we return to the same $U_a$ by a path involving heat flow into the system, there must be net work done in going around the path. Since $\Delta U$ for the cycle is zero, we can sum up the $\Delta Q$ and $\Delta W$ terms as follows:

$$\Delta Q_{return} - \int_{b\,\text{return}}^{a} P\ dV - \int_{a\,\text{irreversible}}^{b} P\ dV = 0 \qquad (6\text{-}35)$$

Equation (6-35) can be rewritten in the following form:

$$\Delta Q_{\text{return}} = \Delta W_{\text{net work around cycle}} \tag{6-36}$$

A device such as we have just described can act cyclically and convert heat into work with no other effect, which is a violation of the engine statement of the second law, hence $\Delta S = S_b - S_a \geqslant 0$ for irreversible processes and $S_b > S_a$. The spontaneous process always leads to a state of higher entropy.

## D. THE MEASURABILITY OF ENTROPY

The entropy of a pure substance can always be determined relative to some arbitrary standard state. If the standard state is defined by some values of the pressure and temperature $P_0$ and $T_0$, any arbitrary state can be represented by some values of $P$ and $T$. Since entropy is an extensive function, and depends on the amount of material in the system, the entropy of pure substances is generally determined as entropy per gram or entropy per mole. We will adopt the convention of using entropy per mole. The starting point is one mole of pure substance (one chemical species only and one phase only) at $P_0$ and $T_0$. A reversible path must be followed to $P$, $T$. First reversibly heat the system at constant pressure from $T_0$ to $T$ and then place it in contact with a reservoir at temperature $T$ and expand or contract the system until the pressure goes from $P_0$ to $P$. The change in entropy is therefore

$$S - S_0 = \int_{T_0}^{T} \frac{dQ}{T} + \int_{P_0}^{P} \frac{dQ}{T} \tag{6-37}$$

Equation (6-37) can be rewritten in the following form:

$$S - S_0 = \int_{T_0}^{T} \frac{(\partial Q/\partial T)_P \, dT}{T} + \frac{1}{T} \int_{P_0}^{P} \left(\frac{\partial Q}{\partial V}\right)_T dV \tag{6-38}$$

The quantity $(\partial Q/\partial T)_p$ is the specific heat at constant pressure $C_p$ while $(\partial Q/\partial V)_T$ is the heat of compression at constant temperature $h_c$. Both of these quantities can be measured by calorimetric methods and values for pure substances are available in the literature. These empirically determined parameters can be inserted into Equation (6-38), leading to

$$S - S_0 = \int_{T_0}^{T} \frac{C_p \, dT}{T} + \frac{1}{T} \int_{P_0}^{P} h_c \, dV \tag{6-39}$$

$C_p$ and $h_c$, as we have already noted, can be determined as functions of temperature and pressure. Equation (6-39) can be evaluated by numerical integration, so that the entropy of a pure substance relative to a standard state can always be determined if the appropriate calorimetry has been done.

In many applications both $P$ and $P_0$ are taken as atmospheric pressure, so that Equation (6-39) reduces to

$$S = S_0 + \int_{T_0}^{T} \frac{C_p \, dT}{T} \tag{6-40}$$

### E. THE THIRD LAW OF THERMODYNAMICS

*The third law of thermodynamics states that the entropy of all pure substances at absolute zero is zero. This law may be viewed as a defining statement for the previously arbitrary standard state for entropy.* It is probably best to regard the third law as a postulate of thermodynamics, as it later takes on special meaning in light of statistical mechanics. Utilizing the third law, Equation (6-40) becomes

$$S = \int_{0}^{T} \frac{C_p \, dT}{T} \tag{6-41}$$

With the use of this equation plus measured values of the specific heat it is possible to calculate the absolute entropy of any pure substance. The values of entropy given in thermodynamic tables are calculated this way. In Chapter XIV we shall briefly outline experimental methods of measuring specific heats.

### F. ENTROPY AND CHEMICAL REACTIONS

Thus far our thermodynamics analysis has been in terms of pure substance or, in one restricted case, in terms of two perfect gases. The next stage is to consider chemical reactions and the associated energy and entropy changes. The method of approach is to go back to the first law of thermodynamics in the form $dU = dQ - P \, dV$. In this form the law states that the change of total energy of a system is the amount of heat crossing the boundaries of the system plus the amount of work crossing the boundaries of the system. Suppose now that a small amount $dn_i$ moles of a pure substance crosses the boundary into the system.

The change of energy of the system due to this process is

$$dU = \left(\frac{\partial U}{\partial n_i}\right)_{S,V} dn_i \qquad (6\text{-}42)$$

This energy will be additive to the energy flows from the other processes, so that we may write the first law for a reversible transformation as

$$dU = T\, dS - P\, dV + \left(\frac{\partial U}{\partial n_i}\right)_{S,V} dn_i \qquad (6\text{-}43)$$

We will define the coefficient of $dn_i$ as the chemical potential of the $i$th substance $\mu_i$,

$$\mu_i = \left(\frac{\partial U}{\partial n_i}\right)_{S,V} \qquad (6\text{-}44)$$

If we now generalize Equation (6-42) for the possibility of many substances, we get

$$dU = T\, dS - P\, dV + \sum \mu_i\, dn_i \qquad (6\text{-}45)$$

The first law is still a conservation law indicating that the change of energy in a system is the sum of all the energy flows in and out of the system. The existence of more than one chemical species introduces a new factor to be considered, the possibility of chemical reactions. Under such considerations the $n_i$ are not conserved; the reversible introduction of $dn_i$ moles of a substance into a system does not necessarily increase the amount of that substance in the system by an amount $dn_i$, as chemical reactions may act as internal sources or sinks for the $i$th substance. Similarly, chemical reactions may act as sources or sinks for thermal energy and potential energy. All this does not affect the validity of Equation (6-45), but merely stresses that $\sum \mu_i\, dn_i$ is not an exact differential in exactly the same sense that $dQ$ and $dW$ are not exact differentials. Another way of viewing this is that energy is conserved, mass is conserved, indeed for ordinary chemical reactions (excluding nuclear reactions) the number of atoms of each type is conserved, but the form of the energy is not conserved and the chemical form of the atoms is not conserved. Changes in chemical form are accompanied by changes in energy form, so that the conservation laws as well as the relations governing change of form are related. With this in mind the notion of $U$ being a state function can be generalized and we can write

$$U = U(S, V, n_i) \qquad (6\text{-}46)$$

In any chemical reaction taking place within the system the $dn_i$ are not independent but are related by the stoichiometry of the reaction. Consider the following chemical transformation taking place in a system in which there is no flow of matter from the outside:

$$aA + bB \rightleftharpoons cC + dD \qquad (6\text{-}47)$$

Equation (6-47) is a representation of any arbitrary chemical reaction in which two reagents react to give two products. The lowercase letters $a$, $b$, $c$, and $d$ are the stoichiometric coefficients and are usually small integers. The capital letters A, B, C, and D are simply the symbols designating the chemical species and in actual cases are represented by chemical formulae. An actual example of an equation of this type is

$$1BaCl_2 + 2NaOH \rightleftharpoons 1Ba(OH)_2 + 2NaCl$$

In order for $a$ moles of A to be used up, they must react with $b$ moles of B to produce $c$ moles of C and $d$ moles of D. Therefore,

$$-\frac{dn_A}{a} = -\frac{dn_B}{b} = \frac{dn_C}{c} = \frac{dn_D}{d} \qquad (6\text{-}48)$$

We can set Equation (6-48) equal to a new function $d\xi$, where $\xi$ is defined as the degree of advancement of a chemical reaction. We can then write

$$dn_A = -a d\xi, \qquad dn_B = -b\, d\xi, \qquad dn_C = c\, d\xi, \qquad dn_D = d\, d\xi \qquad (6\text{-}49)$$

The number of independent variables has been reduced from four to one because of stoichiometric constraints.

The entropy change accompanying a chemical reaction obeys the general conditions regarding entropy that we have just outlined. To look at an example, start with a vessel of constant volume containing molecules of A and B only and in contact with a reservoir at temperature $T$. Next allow the reaction shown in Equation (6-47) to proceed to equilibrium. The entropy change may be split into two parts—that in the vessel and that in the reservoir. In the vessel the entropy change will be

$$\Delta S = S_{\text{final}} - S_{\text{initial}} \qquad (6\text{-}50)$$

If the initial and final states are equilibrium states, an equation of the above form can always be written since $S$ is a state function. If $\Delta Q$ is the heat transferred to the reservoir during the chemical reaction, the entropy change of the reservoir is

$$S_r = \frac{\Delta Q}{T} \qquad (6\text{-}51)$$

The total entropy change of the universe is therefore

$$S_t = S_{\text{final}} - S_{\text{initial}} + \frac{\Delta Q}{T} \qquad (6\text{-}52)$$

If the reaction is carried out along a reversible path, $S_t$ is zero; otherwise, it will be positive, as indicated in our previous considerations of entropy. The formalism of Equation (6-52) provides a useful introduction to free-energy functions and we shall later use it for proving some important theorems about these functions.

We have now completed our introduction to temperature and entropy from the point of view of thermodynamics and kinetic theory. To give deeper meaning to these concepts and ultimately to relate them to biology, we must first consider the approaches of statistical mechanics and the insights of information theory. The next chapter introduces some simple notions of probability and information.

PROBLEMS

1.  Prove that

    $$\left(\frac{\partial T}{\partial V}\right)_S = -\left(\frac{\partial P}{\partial S}\right)_V$$

2.  Assume that in Equation (6-15) we had required that

    $$\left(\frac{\partial U}{\partial S}\right)_V = T^2$$

    Would the resulting entropy function be a state function?

3.  A hen's egg in contact with an infinite isothermal reservoir gives rise to a chick. Discuss the entropy changes. (Hint: Does heat flow from the reservoir to the egg or in the opposite direction?)

4.  If the specific heat of a solid at constant pressure is given by $aT + bT^2 + cT^3$, derive an expression for the entropy as a function of temperature.

# CHAPTER VII

# Probability and Information

*The director of a life insurance company does not know when each of the insured will die, but he relies upon the calculus of probabilities and on the law of great numbers, and he is not deceived, since he distributes dividends to his stockholders.*

from " Chance "

by HENRI POINCARÉ

## A. PROBABILITY

This chapter represents a transition in our thinking from the gross macroscopic behavior of matter to a consideration of the submicroscopic details underlying the phenomenology. A number of conceptual tools must be introduced from probability theory, combinatorial analysis, and information theory. When these have been reviewed it will be possible in the next chapter to go on to a consideration of elementary statistical mechanics.

We begin with the notion of examining the properties of aggregates. In thermal physics, in biology and in many other areas we are frequently called on to deal with collections of quantities, whether they be molecules, experimental data, sequences of computer readouts, or any other sequence of numerical values. Often the quantities of theoretical interest are properties of the aggregates rather than the individual elements. It may happen that, although we are unable to obtain information about the elements, we may still deal effectively with the collection. Statistical mechanics represents such a case, where we are unable to say much about the individual molecules, but are able to make predictions about properties of a group of molecules such as pressure, temperature, and density.

In cases where we may assign numerical values to each of the elements, we may utilize directly certain properties of the aggregate. If we designate the value of the $i$th element in a sequence as $x_i$, the mean, or average value of $x$, of a collection of $n$ elements is given in the following equation:

$$\bar{x} = \frac{\sum_{i=1}^{n} x_i}{n} \tag{7-1}$$

The mean square deviation $\Delta^2$ is given by

$$\Delta^2 = \frac{\sum_{i=1}^{n} (x_i - \bar{x})^2}{n} \tag{7-2}$$

The collection $x_i$ may form either a continuous or a discrete set of numbers. If the set is discrete, we may designate the fraction of the elements with the value $x_j$ as $f(x_j)$. The subscript $i$ numbers the elements in a sequence, while the subscript $j$ refers to all elements in the sequence with a value $x_j$ regardless of where they occur. We may then write

$$f(x_j) = n_j/n \tag{7-3}$$

$$\sum_j f(x_j) = 1 \tag{7-4}$$

where $n_j$ is the number of elements having the value $x_j$. If the $x_i$ may have continuous values, then $f(x) \, dx$ is taken to represent the fraction of elements having values between $x$ and $x + dx$. It then follows that

$$\int_{\substack{\text{all possible}\\ \text{values of } x}} f(x) \, dx = 1 \tag{7-5}$$

In actual practice, if the $x_i$ represent experimental data, the collection is always discrete, as every instrument will have a limiting sensitivity, a certain number of significant figures to which it can be read. This is more clearly seen in digital readout devices than in trying to squint at a pointer on a meter and trying to squeeze out one more significant figure.

The function $f(x_j)$ or $f(x)$ is usually designated as a distribution function. Figure 7-1 represents such a discrete distribution function.

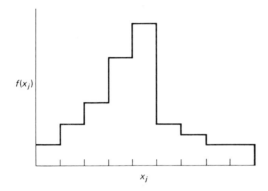

**Fig. 7-1.** Distribution function. The probability that a quantity will have a value $x_j$ is plotted as a function of the value of $x_j$.

If the function $f(x_j)$ has only one maximum, the value of $x_j$ at which it occurs is known as the median. A distribution with a single maximum can either be symmetrically distributed about the mean or can be skewed in its distribution about that point. *A distribution with two maxima is termed bimodal, three maxima form a trimodal distribution, etc.* (definition).

A number of mathematical methods have been devised to deal with aggregates, among them probability analysis, statistics, theory of errors, and information theory. Each of them provides certain background information which is useful in understanding the basic methods of statistical mechanics. We shall therefore pick out and discuss certain topics which will be useful in subsequent chapters.

Probability theory seems to be historically rooted in games of chance, so the reader will realize that we are following a time honored tradition when we introduce the subject by talking about throwing dice. We will begin by asking the question, "What is the chance of throwing a three with a die?" We may answer this question in one of two ways. First, we may reason that there are six possible numbers that may be thrown and, given an "honest" die and an "honest" thrower, each number will have an equally likely chance of turning up, hence in a long series of throws we will expect a three to appear one-sixth of the time. This corresponds to the *a priori* definition of probability, a definition going back to Laplace. Alternatively, we might throw the die a large number of times, record the results, and measure the ratio of threes to the total number of throws and take the limit of this ratio for a long sequence of observations as the chance of throwing a three. This procedure corresponds to the *a posteriori* method of measuring probabilities.

In practical application the first definition is troublesome because of the problem of knowing that we have an " honest " die and an " honest " thrower (the physics and psychology of the situation are in fact too difficult). The second definition is incomplete in being unable to say how many observations are necessary to establish the limit. In addition, it will not serve us where we are unable to measure the elements of a sequence, but may only deal with averages. This will prove to be the case in statistical mechanics, where the situation is handled by assuming certain states to be equally probable and justifying the assumption by the correspondence of theory and experiment.

The question of when we may use probability theory in dealing with an aggregate is a very important one. Below are presented two sequences of numbers:

Sequence  *A*:     1, 2, 3, 4, 5, 6, 1, 2, 3, 4, 5, 6, 1, 2, 3, 4, 5, 6, 1, 2, 3,
                   4, 5, 6, . . . , etc.

Sequence *B*:      1, 4, 3, 1, 4, 1, 6, 1, 3, 6, 2, 5, 1, 5, 2, 4, 1, 6, 2, 5,
                   1, 1, 3, 5, 3, 6, 2, 5, 2, 4, 3, 4, 3, 1, 5, 4, 6, 3, 2, 5,
                   5, 6, 4, 1, 2, 5, 5, 2, 3, 3, 6, 2, 5, 1, 2, 2, 2, 3, 4, 5,
                   6, 6, 3, 2, 5, 4, 3, 2, 5, 5, 6, 3, 4, 5, 6, 1, 1, 4, 6, 5,
                   4, 1, 3, 4, 3, 3, 2, 6, 4, 5, 3, 5, 6, 1, 2, 4, 2, 5, 2, 3,
                   6, 5, 2, 5.

The first sequence was obtained in an obvious manner, the second by the somewhat less obvious manner of throwing dice. The first sequence was formulated by a rule and we can unambiguously state the next element in the sequence, while in the second sequence we can only state the probability of the next element having some particular value. The second sequence is known as a random sequence, and probability is usually limited to such sequences. The notion of randomness is a very important one in physics, yet difficult to describe. (Randomness has become so significant that one of the outstanding scientific publications of recent years was a book of one million random digits.) Often a process is so complicated or we are so ignorant of the boundary conditions, or of the laws governing the process, that we are unable to predict the result of the process in any but a statistical fashion. For instance, suppose we have a collection of radioactive phosphorus atoms, $P^{32}$, and take an individual atom and question how long it will take to emit an electron. Here we do not know the boundary conditions, i.e., the detailed state of the nucleus, nor do we know the exact laws covering radioactive decay. The time can take on any value. We may obtain an aggregate of such values as is done in experiments on radioactive half-lives and deduce certain features of the collection, but we may only make probability statements about the individual atom. Randomness is in a certain sense a consequence of the ignorance of the observer, yet randomness itself displays certain properties which have been turned into powerful tools in the study of the behavior of systems of atoms.

After first reviewing the elementary laws of probability, we shall investigate certain of the properties of random systems which are important in statistical mechanics.

To simplify our discussion of probability, we shall consider at the moment only independent events; that is, given a sequence of elements, we assume that the probability of any one element having a particular value is independent of the values of the other elements in the sequence. Consider first two elements 1 and 2, with the probability of the first element having a specified value $X$ being $P_A(X)$ and that for the second element being $P_B(X)$. Now, in considering the pair there are four possibilities:

1. Both elements will have the value $X$.
2. Neither element will have the value $X$.
3. Element 1 will have the value $X$, but element 2 will not.
4. Element 2 will have the value $X$, but element 1 will not.

The axioms of probability theory give the following probabilities to each of the four cases:

1. Both: $P_1 = P_A(X)P_B(X)$.
2. Neither: $P_2 = [1 - P_A(X)][1 - P_B(X)]$
3. 1 but not 2: $P_3 = P_A(X)[1 - P_B(X)]$
4. 2 but not 1: $P_4 = [1 - P_A(X)]P_B(X)$

Since the two elements must fit one of the four possibilities, the sum of $P_1, P_2, P_3$, and $P_4$ must be unity, as can be verified by adding them. In our use of probability theory we shall proceed from the rules listed above.

B. INFORMATION THEORY

In addition to probability and statistics, a more recent method of handling aggregates is information theory. While historically speaking, statistical mechanics is many decades older than information theory, there is certain justification in treating information theory first. The later theory is more general, applies to any kind of aggregate, and within its context we can develop, in a familiar fashion, certain abstract concepts which are of importance in statistical mechanics. In particular, the entropy function of statistical mechanics can be more easily appreciated after having first comprehended the analogous information function.

Information theory arose in the communications industry, where it was necessary to quantitatively measure the amount of information transmitted in a communication channel. With such a measure it would then be possible to optimize the information per unit energy expenditure or information per unit time or information per unit cost or any other parameter of practical importance in the design of communication networks. The resulting measure of information has had unforeseen consequences on the thinking of a number of disciplines.

Information theory starts with a message, which is a linear array of symbols which, in normal language, may be a set of words, syllables, letters, or phonemes. The theory is quite general and finds application in any linear array of symbols, which may be musical notes, experimental observations, amino acids in a linear peptide, or any other defined sequence.

The notion of information bears very heavily on the area where physical science and psychology overlap. This is a very ill-understood area and confusion can easily arise. An attempt is made to avoid this problem by designing an information measure that is independent of the truth of the message or the meaning of the message but is just related to the formal aspects of transmitting and receiving a set of symbols.

The logic of our approach may be difficult to follow since information is not a physical quantity in the sense that mass, charge, or pressure are physical quantities. Information deals with the usefulness of a set of symbols to an observer. Since information does not measure anything physical, we are free to choose any information measure we please. The definition is therefore at first arbitrary and the choice is based on a common sense estimate of the usefulness of a set of symbols. The original definition arising from the needs of the communications industry was, to use P. W. Bridgman's words, "of such unblushing economic tinge." What in the end turns out to be surprising is that the definition which was introduced is found to relate to the entropy concept in interesting and very fundamental ways. What appears to lie behind all this is the fact that our view of the physical universe is not a cold, lifeless abstraction but is structured by the human mind and the nature of life itself. While it has long been fashionable to inquire how biology depends on the underlying physics, we are being forced to inquire how physics depends on the underlying biology of the mind.

The approach used is to define a measure of the information of an element in a sequence of elements or message. The measure is then shown to accord with some of our intuitive notions about information and to have certain analytical properties which makes it useful. The information measure is ultimately shown to have certain formal relations to the entropy measure of statistical mechanics. Lastly, it is shown that when the information measure relates to which of the possible quantum states a system is in, then the relationship between information and entropy becomes more than just a formal analogy.

*The information content of a symbol is then defined as*

$$I = \ln_2 p_r/p_s \qquad (7\text{-}6)$$

$I$ is the information content of the symbol, $p_s$ is the probability that the symbol was sent and $p_r$ is the probability that the symbol that was sent was correctly received. The logarithm to the base two was originally chosen because relays and electronic devices used in communication networks had two states, on and off. With such components a binary mathematics (Boolean algebra) was the method of choice. With the equipment now in use there is less reason to use arithmetic to the base two, except that, considering the body of existing theory, there seems little reason to change. Note that for any logarithmic base

$$ln_\alpha x = \zeta \ln_2 x \qquad (7\text{-}7)$$

with appropriate algebraic manipulation we can show that

$$\zeta = \frac{1}{\ln_2 \alpha} = \ln_\alpha 2 \qquad (7\text{-}8)$$

It is frequently useful to convert from the $\ln_2$ used in information theory to $\ln_e$, which is the normal exponential base used in calculus, in which case

$$\zeta = \frac{1}{\ln_2 e} = \ln_e 2 = 0.69315 \qquad (7\text{-}9)$$

Next rewrite equation (7-6) as

$$I = -\ln_2 p_s + \ln_2 p_r \qquad (7\text{-}10)$$

The quantity $p_r$, the probability that the message has been received once it has been sent, relates to the fidelity of the communication channel between sender and receiver. For an ideal channel $p_r = 1$, $\ln(p_r) = 0$, and this term makes no contribution to the information measure.

Information, as we have pointed out, is not a physical quantity, but in order to transmit symbols over a communication channel, we must convert them in to some physical form such as electrical pulses, flashes of light, sound waves, or other forms. In the encoding, transmission, and decoding of these signals, errors may occur due to mechanical failure, poorly designed equipment, extraneous signals being introduced from other sources, or from thermal noise. For all real channels $p_r < 1$, $\ln(p_r) < 0$, that is, the failure of the channel to transmit the message with 100% fidelity reduces the information content of the message. The lower the value of $p_r$, the larger the negative value of $\ln(p_r)$ and the more information is lost. This clearly agrees with our intuitive notions of information. A poor transmission line corresponds to low $p_r$ and reduces the amount of information transmitted. In many applications, particularly those which will be of importance to us in relating information theory to thermal physics, $p_r \cong 1$ and we can drop the second term, reducing Equation (7-10) to

$$I = -\ln_2 p_s \qquad (7\text{-}11)$$

This expression is the real heart of information theory and the one that we must relate to our intuitive notions of information. The quantity $p_s$ relates to the entire range of symbols that can comprise the message; that is, $p_s$ is a normalized probability distribution. Designate the probability of the $j$th type of symbol as $p_j$, then

$$\sum_{j=1}^{n} p_j = 1 \qquad (7\text{-}12)$$

Equation (7-12) means that $n$ possible symbols can be sent; that is, the effective alphabet or dictionary contains $n$ symbols. Since an element in the sequence must contain one of the $n$ possibilities, the sum of the probabilities must be one, as in Equation (7-12). Since all probabilities are positive and each is less than one, the information content of a symbol in Equation (7-11) is always positive. If $p_s$ approaches one, $I$

approaches zero; that is, if we were certain what a message was going to be ($p_s = 1$), we would get no additional information by receiving the message.

Suppose $W$ possible messages can be sent and they are all equally probable. Then $p_s = 1/W$ and Equation (7-11) becomes

$$I = -\ln_2 \frac{1}{W} = \ln_2 W \qquad (7\text{-}13)$$

Equation (7-13) says that the more possible messages that can be sent, the greater the information that we have when we receive one of them. The greater the number of messages that can be sent, the more possibilities can be distinguished and the greater the information in knowing which of those possibilities is in fact being indicated by the message.

Returning to Equation (7-11), let us examine a concrete case, where the elements in the sequence are the letters of the alphabet; that is, let us assume that the message is written in ordinary English. The 26 letter have a far from equal probability distribution, as is shown in Table 1.

The conclusion from our definition is that an infrequent letter carries far more information per letter than a common letter. This is a conclusion that has been known for a long time by devotees of crossword puzzles, who know that a rare letter narrows the choice of words far

**TABLE 1**

*Probability Distribution and Information Measure of the Letters of the English Alphabet*

| Letter | $p_i$ | $-\ln_2 p_i$ | Letter | $p_i$ | $-\ln_2 p_i$ |
|--------|-------|--------------|--------|-------|--------------|
| a | 0.0805 | 3.6716 | n | 0.0719 | 3.8364 |
| b | 0.0162 | 6.0080 | o | 0.0794 | 3.6917 |
| c | 0.0320 | 5.0161 | p | 0.0229 | 5.5037 |
| d | 0.0365 | 4.8279 | q | 0.0020 | 9.0565 |
| e | 0.1231 | 3.0525 | r | 0.0603 | 4.0927 |
| f | 0.0228 | 5.5101 | s | 0.0659 | 3.9635 |
| g | 0.0161 | 6.0171 | t | 0.0959 | 3.4166 |
| h | 0.0514 | 4.3256 | u | 0.0310 | 5.0625 |
| i | 0.0718 | 3.8384 | v | 0.0093 | 6.8170 |
| j | 0.0010 | 10.0665 | w | 0.0203 | 5.6792 |
| k | 0.0052 | 7.6365 | x | 0.0020 | 9.0565 |
| l | 0.0403 | 4.6799 | y | 0.0188 | 5.8248 |
| m | 0.0225 | 5.5295 | z | 0.0009 | 10.2202 |

more than a common letter and therefore conveys more information about the missing word.

Equation (7-13) suggests another approach to the problem of information. Suppose the elements in the sequence are words instead of letters. Then, assuming equal probabilities of using words, $W$ represents the total vocabulary of the sender. The information measure says that someone with a large vocabulary can send more information per word than someone with a small vocabulary.

If we allow the elements in the sequence to be letters, then the information content is independent of the vocabulary of the sender; if we allow it to be words, then it is dependent on the vocabulary of the sender. Thus the same message will have a different information content according to how we evaluate it. This seeming paradox relates to the fact that information is not dependent on meaning or truth but is a property of the probability distribution of Equation (7-11). The rules that go into grouping symbols can alter the probability distributions and hence alter the information measure. Information, as we have pointed out, is not a physical quantity that has an absolute measure; it is rather a property of a sequence of elements and depends on certain arbitrary choices for classifying and grouping elements. Information measure thus depends on the classifying and grouping procedure. It thus involves the observer or experimenter in a very intimate way. We are already familiar with the observer being intimately involved in his observation. The uncertainty principle in quantum mechanics and the transformation of special relativity are examples of this. Information theory begins with the observer; after all, information is ultimately a property of the human mind. The theory thus starts with a certain arbitrariness in the choice of what kind of information the observer wants and how he chooses to coarse-grain or fine-grain his observations. When the information becomes information about physical systems rather than information about arbitrary sequences of elements, then the relation of information to physically measurable quantities must be examined. This will be done in Chapter X.

The next step in the development of information theory is the proof of the additivity of the information of two elements in a sequence, and the derivation of the expression of the average information of an element in a long sequence.

Consider a message that contains two symbols $A$ and $B$ which are completely independent. If the probability of sending $A$ is $p_A$ and the probability of sending $B$ is $p_B$, the probability of the joint message $AB$

is given by our probability axioms as $p_A p_B$. The information content of the message $AB$ is thus

$$I_{AB} = -\ln_2 p_A p_B = -\ln_2 p_A - \ln_2 p_B = I_A + I_B \qquad (7\text{-}14)$$

The information content of the combined message is thus the sum of the information contents of the two individual messages.

The average information content of a message of independent, uncorrelated elements is the sum of the information divided by the number of elements. For a message in which the $j$th element occurs $N_j$ times

$$\bar{I} = \sum_j \frac{N_j I_j}{N} = \sum_j \frac{N_j}{N} (-\ln_2 p_j) \qquad (7\text{-}15)$$

As the message gets sufficiently long, the *a posteriori* measure of probability indicates that

$$\frac{N_j}{N} \to p_j \qquad (7\text{-}16)$$

Equation (7-15) then becomes

$$\bar{I} = -\sum p_j \ln_2 p_j \qquad (7\text{-}17)$$

Equation (7-17) is the expression for information that we shall use most frequently.


PROBLEMS

1. A naturally occurring peptide is a sequence of twenty naturally occurring amino acids. If each of the amino acids were equally likely, what would be the information content per amino acid?

2. Nucleic acids are sequences of nucleotides chosen from a group of four possible nucleotides. If each nucleotide was equally probable, what would be the information content per nucleotide?

3. Use the results of problems 1 and 2 and discuss why a minimum of three nucleotides is necessary to code for an amino acid.

4. A hand of cards can be regarded as a sequence of symbols. What is the information content in picking up a royal flush (ace, king, queen, jack, ten of the same suit)?

CHAPTER **VIII**

# Introduction to Statistical Mechanics

*For it is in relation to the statistical point*
*of view that the structure of the vital parts of*
*living organisms differ so entirely from that*
*of any piece of matter that we physicists and*
*chemists have ever handled physically in our*
*laboratories or mentally at our writing desks.*

ERWIN SCHRÖDINGER

in " What is Life? "

Cambridge University Press, 1944

## A. THE STATISTICAL POINT OF VIEW

In thermodynamics we deal with macroscopic measurements, using measuring instruments which are large compared with individual molecules and which have response times long in comparison to the times of individual molecular processes. Small measuring probes of the order of 1 mm contain about $10^{20}$ atoms, while a measurement which takes 1 msec is long in comparison with molecular vibration times, which are the order of $10^{-8}$ sec or less. Thus macroscopic measurements represent averages over a very large number of molecular events. This type of averaging suggests one of the most powerful methods of thermal physics, predicting the macroscopic properties of systems by averaging over all possible solutions of the mechanical system viewed at the atomic level. This general method is designated as statistical mechanics, which by its applications to macromolecules has already made major contributions to biological thought.

To discuss the general ideas, visualize a box of dimensions $L_x$, $L_y$, and $L_z$ which contains $N$ atoms of a perfect gas and is in contact with a thermal reservoir at temperature $T$. The system can be completely described by specifying the position $(x, y, z)$ and momentum $(p_x, p_y, p_z)$ of each of the $N$ particles. Thus $6N$ coordinates are required to completely specify the system at the atomic level. If we construct an abstract $6N$-dimensional space, the instantaneous state of the system can be determined as a single point in this space since a point involves assigning a value to each one of the $6N$ variables. The behavior of the system can be completely described by the trajectory of the point in the $6N$-dimensional space. Any macroscopic measurement averages over a long segment of this trajectory. We cannot, of course, determine this trajectory from first principles, since that would involve an $N$-body problem where $N$ is very large and thus provides insuperable mathematical difficulties.

A given macroscopic system can be visualized in an alternate way. We begin by forming an ensemble; that is, by taking a very large number of identical macroscopic systems and placing them in contact with an isothermal reservoir. The meaning of identical is that all of the systems have the same macroscopic properties (composition, volume, temperature) although they may certainly vary with respect to the actual molecular details. Each system in the ensemble may be represented by a point in our $6N$-dimensional space and the entire ensemble will be represented by a cluster of points. At equilibrium that cluster can be represented by a time-independent density distribution function. We can now calculate any macroscopic average over the ensemble in the following way. With each point in the $6N$-space we may associate a value of the given macroscopic property $M(x_1\, y_1\, z_1, x_2, y_2, z_2, \ldots,)$. The previous assumption follows directly from mechanics. In a small volume $dV$ around the point there are $n\, dV$ members of the ensemble, where $n$ represents the density distribution function. The average of $M$ over the whole ensemble is then

$$\overline{M} = \frac{\int_V Mn\, dV}{\int n\, dV} \qquad (8\text{-}1)$$

The idea of an ensemble is of course a conceptual one since such a large group of systems are being envisioned that we could not actually form an experimental ensemble. The ensemble is thus an abstraction which turns out in some cases to be a remarkably efficient computing device. Since we have defined the member systems by properties such as composition and temperature which have a well-defined meaning only at equilibrium, the ensemble representation that we are using is confined to that condition. This differs from the trajectory representation, which has equal validity for equilibrium and nonequilibrium systems.

Contact is made between the trajectory representation in phase space for equilibrium systems and the ensemble representation by a postulate called the "ergodic hypothesis," which states that for large ensembles and long time trajectories the ensemble representation approaches the trajectory representation; that is, given a small volume of phase space $dV$, the probability of an ensemble point being in that volume is the same as the fraction of time of a long time trajectory in which the phase point falls in that volume. Thus, if we average over the ensemble, we will be able to predict the values to be obtained in a macroscopic measurement.

Before proceeding it might be well to consider a simple analogy which will illustrate the difference between the trajectory and ensemble approaches. Suppose we wish to ask the question: What is the average distance of a worker bee from the beehive during food procurement? We could capture a bee, mount a tiny identifying reflector on him, release him, and take several hours of motion pictures. Each frame would give $r$, the distance as a function of the frame number or time, and we can compute

$$\frac{1}{m} \sum_{i=1}^{m} |r_i|$$

where $i$ is the index number of the photographic frame and $m$ frames are examined. Alternatively, we can take an appropriate aerial photograph and determine the positions of all of the bees visible in the photograph. If the $j$th bee is a distance $r_j$ from the hive, then the average distance is

$$\frac{1}{p} \sum_{j=1}^{p} |r_j|$$

where we average over $p$ bees. The first approach gives us a trajectory average, while the second gives us an ensemble average. How close the two averages would be would depend on the validity of the ergodic theorem for this case.

While analogies of the beehive sort give some feeling for the ensemble approach, they fail to encompass one distinct property unique to molecular systems: macroscopically indistinguishable systems which differ in their detailed mechanical description. It is this feature which makes it impossible for us to go back and forth in any simple way between mechanics and thermodynamics, and forces us to an ultimately statistical approach. With this in mind we can note that the trajectory approach is the straightforward mechanical approach; it assumes the detailed description, the time course of all the atoms and molecules in the system. For real molecular systems this approach is impossibly complicated, so that we invent the ensemble with the assumption that *at equilibrium* the ensemble average of any measurable property will be the same as the time average of that property for a given system. These ideas should become more concrete when we later actually apply the approach to physical problems.

The ergodic hypothesis has been the subject of a large amount of profound consideration from the points of view of physics, mathematics, measurement theory, and philosophy of science. We will avoid the subtleties and disputes in this field by taking a very pragmatic point of view toward the ensemble approach to statistical thermodynamics. We will assume two postulates whose ultimate validity rests solely on the agreement between the predictions of the theory and macroscopic measurements.

1. *The macroscopic properties of systems may be predicted by averaging the property in question over an ensemble of all microstates of the system that are consistent with some set of macroscopic constraints* (postulate).

2. *In performing the averaging, it is usually possible to approximate the average value of a property by its value in the most probable microstate* (postulate). This is equivalent to replacing mean values by median values. This second postulate can in fact be "proved" for the actual distributions of statistical mechanics by a rather sophisticated mathematical technique known as the Darwin–Fowler method of steepest descent.

These two statements on ensemble averaging allow us to make predictive statements provided we can formulate an ensemble of microstates. In classical mechanics the ensemble forms a continuum over all possible coordinates and momenta of the atoms subject to the constraints of the system. This continuum approach leads to certain indeterminacies in evaluating thermodynamic functions. Quantum mechanics seems to form a more natural basis for statistical thermodynamics because the theory itself generates an ensemble of discrete states. Indeed, using the wisdom of hindsight, it has been pointed out that the founders of statistical mechanics might have been alerted to the existence of quantum mechanics by the problem of being able to choose an elementary volume in phase space. We will therefore carry out the actual formal analysis of statistical theory in terms of quantum states, which will necessitate the briefest review of some of the elementary notions of quantum mechanics. We will shortly make some of these notions more concrete by considering the quantum-mechanical problem of the particle in the box. This particular example will later be extended to a collection of particles in a box, which is, of course, the quantum analog of a perfect gas.

## B. The Quantum Mechanical Description of Systems

It should be understood that we cannot here attempt to explain or justify quantum mechanics, but only to present the results so that the notions of quantum state and energy eigenvalue will be more familiar when we utilize them in setting up the fundamental equations of statistical mechanics. The reader interested in more detailed quantum mechanical background should consult a book like *Quantum Mechanics in Chemistry* by M. W. Hanna (Benjamin, New York, 1965).

The formulation of quantum mechanics we shall use was carried out by Erwin Schrödinger, a man who later produced a probing examination of the relationship between biology and the statistical aspects of thermal physics. The starting point of this view of quantum mechanics is the equation for the total energy of a system which we have represented as Equation (2-8) of Chapter II. The equation states that the sum of the potential and kinetic energies of a system equals the total energy. The left side of the equation, the sum of the two energies, is often called the Hamiltonian (definition) and is represented by the symbol $H$. If we designate the total energy of the system by the symbol $E$, we can state the energy conservation principle in the very simple form

$$H = E \tag{8-2}$$

This equation is the starting point for quantum mechanics, which states that for atomic systems the simplified form of the energy equation must be modified. We postulate that the equation $H = E$ must be changed to an operator equation of the form

$$H\psi = E\psi \tag{8-3}$$

where $H$ and $E$ are mathematical operators of a form we will describe and $\psi$ is a function whose values describe the behavior of the system. It should be understood that there is no intuitive way of justifying the use of an operator equation or the actual operators used. The ultimate justification is that the formalism predicts with high precision the observable behavior of atomic and molecular systems.

A mathematical operator is a construct of the form

$$c, \quad \frac{d}{dx}, \quad \frac{d^2}{dx^2}$$

which operates on a function $f$ to yield

$$cf, \quad \frac{df}{dx}, \quad \frac{d^2f}{dx^2}$$

It is a very convenient formalism in a number of areas of theoretical physics.

Returning to Equation (8-3), $H$ is the quantum-mechanical operator that is derived from the classical Hamiltonian, which, as we have noted, is a function equal to the total energy of a system, i.e., the sum of the kinetic and potential energies. Classically, we may write the Hamiltonian for a single particle, $H$, as follows:

$$H = \tfrac{1}{2}mv^2 + V \qquad (8\text{-}4)$$

Frequently problems are formulated in terms of momentum, the product of mass times velocity, instead of in terms of velocity. This turns out to be an especially convenient form for quantum-mechanical problems. Under these circumstances, using $p$ for the momentum, Equation (8-4) becomes

$$H = \frac{p^2}{2m} + V \qquad (8\text{-}5)$$

To put the theory in quantum-mechanical notation, the variables of Equation (8-5) must be transformed into quantum-mechanical operator form. *This it done by a rule which states that each momentum $p_x$ is replaced by an operator*

$$-\frac{ih}{2\pi}\frac{\partial}{\partial x}$$

(postulate). The operator involves $h$, which is Plancks constant; $i$, the square root of minus one (quantum mechanics involves the mathematical methods of complex variables); and $\partial/\partial x$, the partial derivative with respect to $x$. Equations (8-3) and (8-5) become in expanded quantum-mechanical form

$$\frac{-h^2}{8\pi^2 m}\left(\frac{\partial^2 \psi}{\partial x^2} + \frac{\partial^2 \psi}{\partial y^2} + \frac{\partial^2 \psi}{\partial z^2}\right) + V(x, y, z)\psi = E\psi \qquad (8\text{-}6)$$

The successive application of the operator $p$ in the previous equation may be viewed as

$$\begin{aligned}
\frac{p_x{}^2}{2m}\psi &= \frac{1}{2m}\left(-\frac{ih}{2\pi}\frac{\partial}{\partial x}\right)\left(-\frac{ih}{2\pi}\frac{\partial}{\partial x}\right)\psi \\
&= \frac{1}{2m}\left(-\frac{ih}{2\pi}\frac{\partial}{\partial x}\right)\left(-\frac{ih}{2\pi}\frac{\partial \psi}{\partial x}\right) \\
&= \frac{1}{2m}\left(-\frac{ih}{2\pi}\right)^2\frac{\partial^2 \psi}{\partial x^2} = -\frac{h^2}{8\pi^2 m}\frac{\partial^2 \psi}{\partial x^2}
\end{aligned} \qquad (8\text{-}7)$$

Let us again state that we are merely giving an abbreviated statement of a very complicated and sophisticated theoretical approach. The reader is being asked to accept the formalism as a mathematical method which gives the right results. The justification for presenting this material here is the hope that it will convey some notion of a quantum state and an energy eigenvalue, concepts which are the foundation stone of the approach of statistical thermodynamics.

The quantity $E$ represents a constant, the actual energy value of the system. One of the results of quantum mechanics is that physically meaningful solutions of Equation (8-2) can only be obtained for certain discrete values of $E$, which are termed eigenvalues of the energy. This result is in fact the fundamental quantization which imposes the structure on the theory.

The quantity $\psi(x, y, z, t)$ which is a solution to Equations (8-3) or (8-6) is related to the probability of finding the particles at $x, y, z$ at time $t$. In general $\psi$ is a complex number $a + ib$. *For each such number there exists a complex conjugate* $\psi^* = a - ib$ *and the product* $\psi\psi^* = a^2 + b^2$ *is the probability of finding the particle* (postulate). *The function* $\psi$ *must be continuous, single-valued, and the integral of* $\psi\psi^* \, dV$ *over all available space must be one* (postulate); that is, the probability of the particle being somewhere is unity.

As can be seen from Equation (8-6), $\psi$ is a function of $E$ and the restrictions we have just placed on $\psi$ lead to $E$ having discrete allowable values. The existence of the discrete values is the quantization of quantum mechanics; the energy can have only a certain discontinuous set of values and must therefore change by certain quantized amounts. The state $\psi_i$ corresponding to a given allowable energy $E_i$ is designated an eigenstate. The important point is that the system can only exist in a series of discrete states each of which is characterized by an energy eigenvalue. Statistical mechanics consists of a certain kind of enumeration of these states over an appropriate ensemble.

The example we shall use to illustrate the preceding is a particle of mass $m$ in an ideal one-dimensional box. The particle can only move in the $x$ direction between $x = 0$ and $x = L$, where there are infinitely high walls. The potential energy $V(x)$ is shown in Figure 8-1. Inside the box

**Fig. 8-1.** The potential energy curve for a particle in a one-dimensional box. The potential is constant within the box and rises precipitously at the walls.

$V(x)$ is everywhere 0 and at both walls $V(x)$ rises to infinity. Inside the box the fundamental equation of quantum mechanics (8-5) becomes

$$\frac{-h^2}{8\pi^2 m} \frac{\partial^2 \psi}{\partial x^2} = E\psi \tag{8-8}$$

The particle cannot actually be located at either wall, since its energy would go to infinity at those two points. We therefore require that $\psi = 0$ at $x = 0$ and $x = L$. The solution of Equation (8-8) that will turn out to have the properties we desire is

$$\psi = A \sin \alpha x \tag{8-9}$$

where

$$\alpha^2 = \frac{8\pi^2 m E}{h^2} \tag{8-10}$$

The reader can of course verify that Equation (8-9) is a solution of Equation (8-8) by substituting expressions (8-9) and (8-10) into (8-8). This solution always vanishes at $x = 0$. In order for it to vanish at $x = L$, we require that

$$\alpha L = n\pi \qquad (8\text{-}11)$$

The quantity $n$ may be any integer. That is, the sine of $n\pi$ is always zero for any integral value of $n$. Equations (8-10) and (8-11) can be combined to give the following expression:

$$\frac{n^2\pi^2}{L^2} = \alpha^2 = \frac{8\pi^2 mE}{h^2} \qquad (8\text{-}12)$$

We now see that, from Equation (8-12), $E$ cannot take on any values but is given by

$$E = \frac{n^2 h^2}{8mL^2} \qquad (8\text{-}13)$$

where $n$ takes on only integral values. The quantity $n$ is designated the quantum number and the $E(n)$ are the eigenvalues of the energy.

The particle in the box is characteristic of a broad range of quantum-mechanical problems where the solutions form a quantized set. If we now return to the ensemble approach, we may now formulate the problem in the following way. We wish to investigate a macroscopic system that is characterized by specifying the composition and volume, and placing the system in contact with an isothermal reservoir. In principle (but not in practice) we could write down a complete equation of the form of Equation (8-3) for any system. The solutions would then indicate all possible states of the system consistent with the constraints. A given system would be described as completely as we are able to if we specify which quantum state it is in; that is, which $\psi$ function describes the system.

## C. THE ENSEMBLE APPROACH

For an ensemble of $N$ systems each macroscopically identical the most complete description we can give is to specify which quantum state each member system is in. Since we are only interested in averages over the entire ensemble, the quantities we desire to know are how many of the $N$ systems are in each quantum state. For the $j$th state we will

designate this number as $N_j$. The task of statistical mechanics is to determine the $N_j$ or the ratios $N_j/N$, which are usually designated $f_j$, the
probability that a system will be in the $j$th state.

To proceed with the analysis, the ensemble is rearranged in the
following way: all of the members are removed from contact with the
isothermal reservoir, placed in contact with each other, and enclosed in
an adiabatic envelope. This rearrangement is a thought experiment, a
conceptual device, since we never actually experimentally assemble the
ensembles of statistical analysis. From the point of each individual system the boundary conditions remain unchanged since the $N - 1$ remaining systems constitute a large isothermal reservoir at average
temperature $T$, as they were all in contact with a reservoir of temperature
$T$ at the time of isolation. It is now possible to write two equations of
constraint for the ensemble:

$$\sum_j N_j = N \tag{8-14}$$

$$\sum_j N_j E_j = E_T \tag{8-15}$$

It should be noted that a given system remains in a given quantum state
for a very short time and then, by interaction with the wall or internal
interaction, goes over into another quantum state. The set of $N_j$ used
in this analysis refers to the instantaneous distribution over the ensemble. The first equation describes the conservation of systems, while
the second reflects the fact that the adiabatic enclosure results in the
total energy within the enclosure being a constant.

We next introduce one of the fundamental postulates of statistical
mechanics: *for the adiabatically isolated system all possible quantum
states of that system have the same a priori probabilities.* This postulate
refers to the large system which is adiabatically isolated, not to the small
subsystems which can exchange energy with each other. A state of the
large system is completely specified if we specify the quantum states of
each of the small systems which comprise it. The assignment of quantum
states to the small systems must be consistent with Equations (8-14)
and (8-15).

D. THE MOST PROBABLE DISTRIBUTION

In general we are interested in averages over the ensemble, so that it
is not important to know which individual systems are in any given

quantum state, but only how many systems are in that quantum state. What we ultimately wish to know are the average values of $N_j$ for the ensemble.

In general any set of $N_j$'s can occur in many different ways since different sets of assignments of $j$'s to the individual systems can result in the same $N_j$. That is, suppose 3 systems of the ensemble are in the $j$th state. This can happen by having the 1st, 2nd, and 3rd systems in that state or the 1st, 19th, and 23rd, or the 4th, 17th, and 95th, or any other such set. The question we then ask is how many ways can we have $N_1$ systems in the first state, $N_2$ systems in the second state, $N_3$ in the third state, etc., independent of which $N_1$ systems are in the first state, etc. This is an old problem in combinatorial analysis and the answer for $W$, the number of ways, is

$$W = \frac{N!}{N_1! N_2! N_3! \cdots N_r!} = \frac{N!}{\prod_{i=1}^{r} N_i!} \qquad (8\text{-}16)$$

The symbol $N!$ is read "$N$ factorial" and designates the product $N \times (N-1) \times (N-2) \times (N-3) \cdots 3 \times 2 \times 1$.

Since all distributions consistent with Equations (8-14) and (8-15) have equal *a priori* probabilities, the most probable set of $N_j$'s is the one that can occur in the largest number of ways, i.e., the one with the largest value of $W$. We have already indicated that the average state of the system approximates the most probable state of the system. Our task then becomes the maximization of $W$ subject to the constraining equations (8-14) and (8-15). For reasons of analytical convenience we will deal with $\ln W$ rather than $W$ itself. However, the maximum of the logarithm of a function occurs at the same value of the variables as does the maximum of the function, so the essential problem is unchanged by the use of logarithms. We rewrite Equation (8-16),

$$\ln W = \ln\left(\frac{N!}{\prod_i N_i!}\right) = \ln N! - \ln \prod_i N_i!$$
$$= \ln N! - \sum \ln N_i! \qquad (8\text{-}17)$$

The notation $\prod_i N_i!$ is the serial product of $N_1!$ times $N_2!$ times $N_3!$, etc., up to $N_r!$. The second term in Equation (8-17) comes about as the logarithm of a product is the sum of the logarithms. Factorials are very difficult to deal with analytically, so that Equation (8-17) presents a considerably difficult mathematical problem. However, for large values of $N$ and $N_j$ we are able to simplify the expressions by the use of a device known as Stirling's approximation, which states

$$\ln x! \cong x \ln x - x \tag{8-18}$$

This relationship is extremely important in the mathematical simplification of statistical mechanics and is proved in Appendix IV. When we use this approximation in Equation (8-17) it becomes

$$\ln W = N \ln N - N - \sum N_j \ln N_j + \sum N_j \tag{8-19}$$

Substituting Equation (8-14) into Equation (8-19) yields

$$\ln W = N \ln N - \sum N_j \ln N_j \tag{8-20}$$

The mathematical problem now before us is to find a set of values $N_j$ which satisfy Equations (8-14) and (8-15) and maximize $\ln W$ in Equation (8-20). There is a technique known as Lagrange's method of undetermined multipliers which has been designed just for problems of this nature and we shall proceed with a brief exposition of the formal mathematical problem.

   Start with a function $f(x_1, x_2, \ldots, x_r)$ which is to be maximized subject to two constraining equations

$$g(x_1, x_2, \ldots, x_r) = 0, \qquad h(x_1, x_2, \ldots, x_r) = 0 \tag{8-21}$$

Finding an extremum of the function $f$ means that $df$ must be set equal to zero,

$$df = \left(\frac{\partial f}{\partial x_1}\right) dx_1 + \left(\frac{\partial f}{\partial x_2}\right) dx_2 \cdots \left(\frac{\partial f}{\partial x_r}\right) dx_r = 0 \tag{8-22}$$

The equations of constraint can also be written in differential form:

$$dg = \left(\frac{\partial g}{\partial x_1}\right) dx_1 + \left(\frac{\partial g}{\partial x_2}\right) dx_2 + \cdots \left(\frac{\partial g}{\partial x_r}\right) dx_r = 0$$

$$dh = \left(\frac{\partial h}{\partial x_1}\right) dx_1 + \left(\frac{\partial h}{\partial x_2}\right) dx_2 + \cdots \left(\frac{\partial h}{\partial x_r}\right) dx_r = 0 \tag{8-23}$$

We may eliminate two variables by multiplying $dg$ by $\alpha$ and $dh$ by $\beta$ and adding these equations to Equation (8-22):

$$\left(\frac{\partial f}{\partial x_1} + \alpha \frac{\partial g}{\partial x_1} + \beta \frac{\partial h}{\partial x_1}\right) dx_1 + \left(\frac{\partial f}{\partial x_2} + \alpha \frac{\partial g}{\partial x_2} + \beta \frac{\partial h}{\partial x_2}\right) dx_2$$

$$+ \left(\frac{\partial f}{\partial x_3} + \alpha \frac{\partial g}{\partial x_3} + \beta \frac{\partial h}{\partial x_3}\right) dx_3 + \cdots + \left(\frac{\partial f}{\partial x_r} + \alpha \frac{\partial g}{\partial x_r} + \beta \frac{\partial h}{\partial x_r}\right) dx_r = 0 \tag{8-24}$$

$\alpha$ and $\beta$ are at the moment undetermined multipliers, but we shall choose their values so that at the extremum of $f$ they will make the first two coefficients of Equation (8-24) vanish,

$$\frac{\partial f}{\partial x_1} + \alpha \frac{\partial g}{\partial x_1} + \beta \frac{\partial h}{\partial x_1} = 0, \qquad \frac{\partial f}{\partial x_2} + \alpha \frac{\partial g}{\partial x_2} + \beta \frac{\partial h}{\partial x_2} = 0 \qquad (8\text{-}25)$$

Equation (8-24) then becomes

$$\sum_{j=3}^{r} \left( \frac{\partial f}{\partial x_j} + \alpha \frac{\partial g}{\partial x_j} + \beta \frac{\partial h}{\partial x_j} \right) dx_j = 0 \qquad (8\text{-}26)$$

The remaining $dx_j$ are all independent, since we have gone from three equations in $r$ variables to one equation in $r - 2$ variables. Since each $dx_j$ can be varied independently, the only way that (8-26) can be satisfied, therefore, is that

$$\frac{\partial f}{\partial x_j} + \alpha \frac{\partial g}{\partial x_j} + \beta \frac{\partial h}{\partial x_j} = 0, \qquad j = 3, 4, \ldots, r \qquad (8\text{-}27)$$

Equations (8-25) and (8-27) now give $r$ equations in $r$ variables $x_1, \ldots, x_r$ and two undetermined multipliers $\alpha$ and $\beta$. We can therefore solve for each $x_j$ as a function of $\alpha$ and $\beta$. These solutions can be substituted back in the equations of constraint (8-21) and we end up with two equations in two variables $\alpha$ and $\beta$ which can then be solved. Substituting the values of $\alpha$ and $\beta$ determines the values of $x_j$ which solve the original problem.

## E. The Maxwell–Boltzmann Distribution

The method of Lagrange may now be applied to maximize $\ln W = N \ln N - \sum N_j \ln N_j$ subject to $\sum N_j = N$ and $\sum N_j E_j = E_T$.

Before getting lost in a sea of equations it is well at this point to review verbally what we have done. First, we have recognized that in principle the most detailed physical description we can give of a system is to note which quantum state it is in. Second, we note that any macroscopic measurement is a time average over a very large succession of quantum states. Third, we set up an ensemble, which is a calculating device to approximate the very large succession of quantum states. This calculating device consists of a large array of simultaneous systems (subject to the same boundary conditions) all packed in an adiabatic box. We then assert that all possible quantum states of the big box are equally likely and ask what this implies about the individual systems.

We find that three things are implied: (1) conservation of systems [Equation (8-14)]; (2) conservation of energy [Equation (8-15)]; and (3) the large system being in its most probable configuration [a maximization of Equation (8-20)]. We then developed a mathematical method, undetermined multipliers, which allowed us to solve for all three conditions simultaneously. We are now ready to apply that mathematical method to the actual ensemble equations.

We start out by seeking an extremum to $\ln W$ and we write

$$d \ln W = -\sum \ln N_j \, dN_j - \sum dN_j = 0 \qquad (8\text{-}28)$$

This is exactly analogous to Equation (8-22). The analogs to Equation (8-23) are the derivatives of the equation of constraint and are presented below.

$$\sum dN_j = 0 \qquad (8\text{-}29)$$

$$\sum E_j \, dN_j = 0 \qquad (8\text{-}30)$$

We multiply by the undetermined multipliers and then add the equations [as in Equation (8-24)]. The sum is

$$\sum_j \left[ (\alpha - 1) + \beta E_j - \ln N_j \right] dN_j = 0 \qquad (8\text{-}31)$$

This condition requires that

$$\alpha - 1 + \beta E_j - \ln N_j = 0 \qquad (8\text{-}32)$$

Equation (8-32) can be solved directly for $N_j$:

$$N_j = e^{\alpha - 1} e^{\beta E_j} \qquad (8\text{-}33)$$

In principle, the $N_j$ could now be substituted into (8-12) and (8-13) to determine $\alpha$ and $\beta$. This is not usually done, since $E_T$ and $N$ are in general not known. We can eliminate $\alpha$, however, by substituting (8-33) into (8-14),

$$\sum e^{\alpha - 1} e^{\beta E_j} = N \qquad (8\text{-}34)$$

$$e^{\alpha - 1} = \frac{N}{\sum e^{\beta E_j}} \qquad (8\text{-}35)$$

We have now expressed $\alpha$ as a function of $\beta$ and $N$. Substituting back into Equation (8-33), we get

$$N_j = \frac{N e^{\beta E_j}}{\sum e^{\beta E_j}} \qquad (8\text{-}36)$$

Since we are interested only in the ratio $N_j/N$ rather than the absolute value of $N_j$, we may write

$$f_j = \frac{N_j}{N} = \frac{e^{\beta E_j}}{\sum e^{\beta E_j}} \qquad (8\text{-}37)$$

This leaves $\beta$ as the sole undetermined parameter. The evaluation of $\beta$ must be deferred until we come to the comparison of statistical mechanics with thermodynamics.

The next item of business is to derive Equation (8-37) from a different point of view utilizing the notions of information theory. The mathematical manipulations will be very similar to those that we have just gone through, but the slightly different meanings ascribed to the concepts may impart some insight into the methods of statistical physics. Again start with an ensemble of macroscopically identical systems which are characterized by a complete set of quantum states. The information we wish to obtain is what fraction of the members of the ensemble $f_j$ are in the $j$th quantum state. Since the $f_j$ are a normalized probability distribution, we can write

$$\sum f_j = 1 \qquad (8\text{-}38)$$

Since the members of the ensemble are each characterized by an internal energy $U$, we can consider that ensemble members have some average energy,

$$\bar{E} = \sum f_j E_j \qquad (8\text{-}39)$$

In order to view the problem from the point of view of information theory, assume for a moment that one could examine each member of the ensemble and determine what quantum state it was in. The set of quantum states would constitute a message and the average information content of knowing which quantum state a system is in is given by

$$I = -\sum f_j \ln f_j \qquad (8\text{-}40)$$

The preceding formula comes directly from Equation (7-17). The least committal statement I can make about the system is that such a measurement would give a maximum amount of information. That is, if I knew nothing more about the system other than Equations (8-38) and (8-39), then I would anticipate that an otherwise unconstrained system would maximize $I$ subject to these constraints. Therefore, the $f_j$ can be determined by finding a maximum of $I$ by the method of undetermined multipliers. The procedure is formally identical to the one we have just carried out and leads to Equation (8-37).

Both the most-probable-state approach and the information-theory approach lead to the same distribution function for quantum states of the system. In the next chapter we shall study the relationship between the $E_j$ and $f_j$ and the measurable parameters of macroscopic thermodynamics.

### PROBLEMS

1. By direct substitution, show that Equations (8-9) and (8-10) are in fact a solution to Equation (8-8).

2. Calculate $\ln x!$ using the exact expression and the approximation of Equation (8-18) for $x = 4$, $x = 5$, $x = 6$, $x = 7$, $x = 8$, $x = 9$. Comment on how large $x$ has to be for Equation (8-16) to be a good approximation.

3. From a consideration of Equations (8-32)–(8-35) and a consideration of dimensions, what can be said about $\beta$?

4. Comment on the type of distribution to be expected (1) if $\beta$ is negative; (2) if $\beta$ is positive.

# CHAPTER IX

# The Relation between
# Statistical Mechanics and Thermodynamics

*I long ago lost a hound, a bay horse, and a
turtledove, and I am still on their trail. Many
are the travellers I have spoken concerning
them, describing their tracks and what calls
they answered to. I have met one or two who
had heard the hound, and the tramp of the
horse, and even seen the dove disappear behind
a cloud, and they seemed as anxious to recover
them as if they had lost them themselves.*

from " Walden " by
HENRY DAVID THOREAU

## A. EQUIVALENT FORMULATIONS

Our presentation of statistical mechanics in the previous chapter
provides a method of dealing with ensembles of systems distributed over
quantum states; however, until we identify $\beta$ we have no method of
using the theory to make macroscopic predictions. By way of preempting
later developments, we might note that nowhere in the theory have we
explicitly introduced the temperature of the reservoir $T$. Since we would
anticipate different distributions over possible quantum states as a function of temperature, we might guess that $\beta$ will be a function of $T$.

Contact between statistical mechanics and thermodynamics is first made by identifying the internal energy of a system with its average energy over the ensemble,

$$U \leftrightarrow \bar{E} = \frac{E_T}{N} = \sum f_j E_j \qquad (9\text{-}1)$$

$U$ is the total energy of the system and $E_j$ is the total energy of the system in the $j$th quantum state. If the macroscopic measurement of $U$ averages over a sufficient number of quantum states, $\bar{E}$ and $U$ become measures of the same quantity. We may then write

$$U = \sum f_j E_j \qquad (9\text{-}2)$$

For a single homogeneous substance in contact with an isothermal reservoir we may apply the simplest form of the first law of thermodynamics:

$$dU = T \, ds - P \, dV \qquad (9\text{-}3)$$

Equating Equations (9-2) and (9-3), we find that

$$T \, dS - P \, dV = \sum E_j \, df_j + \sum f_j \, dE_j \qquad (9\text{-}4)$$

In simple systems the energy levels $E_j$ are primarily functions of the dimensions of the system, as we have shown in Equation (8-13) of the last chapter. Consider a change in one dimension only. Then we have

$$dE_j = \frac{\partial E_j}{\partial x} \, dx \qquad (9\text{-}5)$$

In order to make Equation (9-5) somewhat more meaningful, let us consider a specific case of a rectangular box of gas whose sides are parallel to the three axes of a coordinate system (see Figure 9-1). In order to change the dimensions by an amount $dx$, we must apply a pressure $P$ on the $yz$ face and do an amount of work $P \, dV$. If the box is adiabatically isolated, the change in energy of the system is $P \, dV$, which must be equal to the change of energy in quantum-mechanical terms, which is $dE_j$. Since $dV$ is $yz \, dx$, we can then write

$$P \, dV = Pyz \, dx = \frac{\partial E_j}{\partial x} \, dx = dE_j \qquad (9\text{-}6)$$

However, $P$ in Equation (9-6) is the specific pressure when the system is in the $j$th quantum state and should consequently be designated as $P_j$.

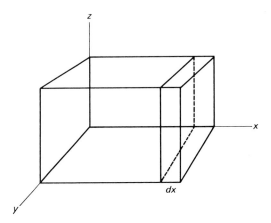

**Fig. 9-1.** A rectangular box of gas oriented along the coordinate axes. The problem of interest is the change in energy accompanying a small change in the $x$ dimension of the box.

The last term in Equation (9-4) then becomes

$$\sum f_j \, dE_j = -\sum f_j P_j \, dV = -dV \sum f_j P_j \qquad (9\text{-}7)$$

The quantity $\sum f_j P_j$ is the ensemble average of the pressure, which we can identify with the macroscopic pressure $P$. Therefore the right-hand term of Equation (9-7) is simply $P \, dV$, and Equation (9-4) reduces to

$$T \, dS = \sum E_j \, df_j \qquad (9\text{-}8)$$

However, from Equation (8-37) of Chapter VIII we note that

$$E_j = \frac{\ln f_j + \ln \sum e^{\beta E_j}}{\beta} \qquad (9\text{-}9)$$

Substituting Equation (9-9) into Equation (9-8) we get

$$T \, dS = \frac{\sum \ln f_j \, df_j}{\beta} + \frac{(\ln \sum e^{\beta E_j})}{\beta} \sum df_j \qquad (9\text{-}10)$$

The second term on the right can be dropped since we have already noted $\sum f_j = 1$, so that $\sum df_j = 0$. Utilizing this result, we can rewrite Equation (9-10) in a somewhat more simplified form as

$$dS = \frac{1}{\beta T} d(\sum f_j \ln f_j) \qquad (9\text{-}11)$$

**00740**

The function $\sum f_j \ln f_j$ may be represented as $X$, in which case Equation (9-11) becomes

$$dS = \frac{1}{\beta T} dX \qquad (9\text{-}12)$$

At this point we introduce properties of the entropy function which allow us to solve Equation (9-11) for $\beta$ and also to solve for the integrated form of $S$. The first restriction is that the entropy function in thermodynamics must be an exact integral. The mathematical requirement on Equation (9-12) is then

$$\frac{1}{\beta T} = f(X) \qquad (9\text{-}13)$$

If Equation (9-13) is satisfied, $dS$ becomes $f(X)\, dX$, which in principle can always be integrated. One further requirement on the entropy function, that of additivity, allows us to solve Equations (9-12) and (9-13) and determine $\beta$. The specification of $\beta$ then completes the identification of thermodynamic and statistical theories and provides the generalized background to go on to more specific applications.

We shall not solve the problem in detail, owing to the mathematical complexities necessary for a rigorous solution. A discussion of this point may be found in *An Introduction to Statistical Mechanics.* by Terrell L. Hill (Addison-Wesley, Reading, Massachusetts, 1960). We shall quote the result, which is that the only function $f(X)$ which permits Equation (9-12) to conform to the additivity postulate is that $f(X)$ is a constant, which we shall designate as $-k$. The fact that the additivity condition holds between any two systems requires that $k$ be a universal constant. Equations (9-12) and (9-13) then lead to the result

$$\beta = -\frac{1}{kT} \qquad (9\text{-}14)$$

Equation (8-37) of Chapter VIII now becomes

$$f_j = \frac{e^{-E_j/kT}}{\sum e^{-E_j/kT}} \qquad (9\text{-}15)$$

and the entropy function $S$ becomes

$$S = -k \sum f_i \ln f_i \qquad (9\text{-}16)$$

## B. The Partition Function

The denominator of Equation (9-15) is a particularly important quantity in statistical mechanics and is usually designated the partition function $Z$, which may formally be defined as

$$Z = \sum e^{-E_i/kT} \qquad (9\text{-}17)$$

The function $Z$ is a hybrid notion combining the $E_i$, which are eigenvalues from quantum mechanics, with $T$, the temperature from phenomenological thermodynamics, and $k$, the quantity which was introduced in the connecting of statistical mechanics with classical thermodynamics. We shall prove that, once $Z$ is known, all the thermodynamic information about a system can be obtained. This is a particularly important notion since it demonstrates the consistency of our various approaches. Start by writing the probability $f_j$ in terms of $Z$ and $E_j$:

$$f_j = \frac{e^{-E_j/kT}}{Z} \qquad (9\text{-}18)$$

We then take the logarithm

$$\ln f_j = \frac{-E_j}{kT} - \ln Z \qquad (9\text{-}19)$$

Substitute Equation (9-19) into the expression for entropy given in Equation (9-16),

$$S = -k \sum f_j \left( -\frac{E_j}{kT} - \ln Z \right) \qquad (9\text{-}20)$$

## C. Helmholtz Free Energy

Rearranging terms in Equation (9-20), we get

$$-kT \ln Z = \sum f_j E_j - TS \qquad (9\text{-}21)$$

The quantity $\sum f_j E_j$ has already been identified as $U$, the internal energy. *The right-hand side of the equation* $(U - TS)$ *will be designated A, the Helmholtz free energy* (definition). From Equation (9-21) we can then write

$$A = -kT \ln Z = U - TS \qquad (9\text{-}22)$$

Thus if $Z$ is known, $A$ is known; that is, the thermodynamic function is directly available from the partition function, since $T$ and $S$ are state functions. Taking the differential, we get

$$dA = dU - T\,dS - S\,dT \qquad (9\text{-}23)$$

Substituting the appropriate form of $dU$ for a multicomponent system $(T\,dS - P\,dV + \sum \mu_i\,dn_i)$, we get

$$dA = -P\,dV + \sum \mu_i\,dn_i - S\,dT \qquad (9\text{-}24)$$

Since $A$ is a state function, we can also write $dA$ in the form of an exact differential

$$dA = \left(\frac{\partial A}{\partial V}\right)_{n_i,T} dV + \sum \left(\frac{\partial A}{\partial n_i}\right)_{V,T,n_j} dn_i + \left(\frac{\partial A}{\partial T}\right)_{n_i,V} dT \qquad (9\text{-}25)$$

From (9-24 and 9-25) we get

$$P = -\left(\frac{\partial A}{\partial V}\right)_{n_i,T}, \qquad \mu_i = \left(\frac{\partial A}{\partial n_i}\right)_{V,T,n_j}, \qquad S = -\left(\frac{\partial A}{\partial T}\right)_{n_i,V} \qquad (9\text{-}26)$$

Thus if we know $Z(V, n_i, T)$, we can derive all other thermodynamic information.

In developing statistical mechanics, we started out with a quantum-mechanical description of the individual members of the ensemble, so that the partition function we arrived at depends upon the eigenvalues. Since the quantum-mechanical description is the best representation of a system which we have, our approach has been fundamentally correct. The difficulty with this approach is that for complex systems it is often very difficult to solve for the eigenvalues and the summations do not always lead to convenient analytical expressions. Where the eigenvalues are closely spaced it is sometimes possible to replace the summation of Equation (9-17) with an integral.

## D. CLASSICAL STATISTICAL MECHANICS

Alternatively, it is possible to formulate statistical mechanics from a classical point of view and to apply it directly to those areas where classical mechanics gives a reasonably good approximation to quantum mechanics. For classical systems the energy $E$ is a function of the co-ordinates and momenta of the particles. If we have $N$ particles, we can then formulate a $6N$-dimensional space in which the dimensions represent the coordinates and momenta of all particles in the system. A point in this phase space then represents a complete classical description of an individual system and an ensemble is represented by a cluster of points in this space. If we now divide the phase space up into a group of small subvolumes and assign a number $i$ to each subvolume, then to each subvolume there corresponds an energy $E_i$,

$$E_i = E(p_i, q_i) \tag{9-27}$$

If we now designate the number of systems of an ensemble whose representative point is in the $i$th subvolume as $N_i$, we can then proceed exactly as in Chapter VIII, Equations (8-28)–(8-33) and get the same representation subject to the fact that the exact size of the subvolume is arbitrary. The resultant equations are the same. In computing the partition functions, we can go from the sum to the integral in the following way:

$$Z = \sum \exp - \frac{E_j}{kT} = \frac{1}{\tau} \int \exp - \frac{E(p, q)}{kT} \, dp \, dq \tag{9-28}$$

$\tau$ is the volume of an element in phase space and cannot be determined from classical mechanics. (From a comparison of classical and quantum theory we know that $\tau = h^{3N}$, where $h$ is Planck's constant.) To evaluate $Z$ in a specific case we note that for a perfect gas

$$E = \sum_j \frac{p_{xj}^2 + p_{yj}^2 + p_{zj}^2}{2m} \tag{9-29}$$

Equation (9-29) says that all the energy is kinetic, and for each particle is the sum of three terms of the form $\frac{1}{2}mv_x^2$, which may be written in momentum notation as $p_x^2/2m$. We may now substitute Equation (9-29) into Equation (9-28) and integrate. There is one integral of six dimensions for each particle, and the partition function is the product of these for $N$ particles.

$$Z = \frac{1}{h^{3N}} \left[ \int_{\substack{\text{all possible values} \\ \text{of coordinates} \\ \text{and momenta}}} \exp - \frac{p_x^2 + p_y^2 + p_z^2}{2mkT} \, dp \, dq \right]^N \tag{9-30}$$

$$= \left[ \left( \frac{2\pi mkT}{h^2} \right)^{3/2} V \right]^N$$

The details of this integration are presented in Appendix V, and Equation (9-30) simply records the results.

We can now proceed to derive some of the thermodynamic properties from $Z$. The Helmholtz free energy now becomes

$$A = -kT \ln Z = -kTN \left[ \ln V + \frac{3}{2} \ln \frac{2\pi mkT}{h^2} \right] \qquad (9\text{-}31)$$

Using the formalism developed in Equation (9-26), we get

$$P = -\frac{\partial A}{\partial V} = \frac{kTN}{V} = \frac{nRT}{V} \qquad (9\text{-}32)$$

Equation (9-32) is the familiar perfect-gas law, which has now been derived from the classical partition function using the formalism of statistical mechanics.

Since there is no interaction potential for molecules of a perfect gas, Equation (9-30) can be regarded as the $N$-fold product of partition functions for a single molecule,

$$Z = z^N$$

$$z = \left( \frac{2\pi mkT}{h^2} \right)^{3/2} V \qquad (9\text{-}34)$$

### E. Velocity Distribution Function

Consider next the velocity distribution in a perfect gas. The probability that an individual molecule has a velocity between $v_x$ and $v_x + dv_x$, $v_y$ and $v_y + dv_y$, $v_z$ and $v_z + dv_z$, and lies between $x$ and $x + dx$, $y$ and $y + dy$, $z$ and $z + dz$ is given by

$$dp(v_x, v_y, dv_z, x, y, z)$$

$$= \frac{m^3}{h^3} \left[ \exp - \frac{m(v_x^2 + v_y^2 + v_z^2)}{2kT} \right] dv_x \, dv_y \, dv_z \, dx \, dy \, dz / Z \qquad (9\text{-}35)$$

In writing Equation (9-35) we have gone from momentum representation to velocity representation. This equation is the classical analog of Equation (9-18) when applied to a perfect–gas molécule. If we wish to consider just the velocity distribution, we integrate the numerator of Equation (9.35) over $dx \, dy \, dz$. This integral is simply the volume $V$. Substituting for $Z$ from Equation (9-34) and rearranging, we get

$$dp(v_x, v_y, v_z) = \frac{\exp[-m(v_x^2 + v_y^2 + v_z^2)/2kT] \, dv_x \, dv_y \, dv_z}{(2\pi kT/m)^{3/2}} \qquad (9\text{-}36)$$

Equation (9-36) is a velocity distribution function for molecules of a perfect gas. It is usually expressed in a somewhat different fashion. We can ask what is the probability that the velocity in the $x$ direction lies between $v_x$ and $v_x + dv_x$ independent of the $y$ and $z$ velocities. To obtain this, we integrate Equation (9-36) over $y$ and $z$. This leads to

$$dp(v_x) = \frac{\exp(-mv_x^2/2kT)\, dv_x}{(2\pi kT/m)^{1/2}} \tag{9-37}$$

Alternately, we might ask what is the probability that a molecule has a speed $v$ independent of the $x$, $y$, and $z$ components of the velocity. Consider a representative point in a phase space of coordinates $v_x$, $v_y$, and $v_z$. We note from geometrical considerations that $v^2 = v_x^2 + v_y^2 + v_z^2$; that is, the square of the velocity is equal to the sum of the squares of its components along the three axes. A particle whose velocity lies between $v$ and $v + dv$ will be represented by a point lying in a spherical shell between $v$ and $v + dv$. The element of volume $dv_x\, dv_y\, dv_z$ is therefore replaced in $v$ notation by $4\pi v^2\, dv$. Rewriting Equation (9-36) in $v$ notation leads to

$$dp(v) = \frac{[\exp(-mv^2/2kT)]4\pi v^2\, dv}{(2\pi kT/m)^{3/2}} \tag{9-38}$$

Equations (9-37) and (9-38) are the Maxwell velocity distribution and are of fundamental importance in understanding the behavior of matter at the molecular level.

The Maxwell velocity distribution emerges from a rather lengthy and abstract set of arguments in statistical mechanics and thermodynamics. Yet it gives a very detailed prediction of how the velocity distribution of perfect-gas molecules depends on temperature and molecular mass. The experimental validity of the velocity distribution should then provide a rather probing examination of the validity of a chain of reasoning. If Equation (9-38) can be shown to correspond to the actual experimental distribution of velocities, it will be strong evidence that our method of approach has been essentially correct. If, on the other hand, Equation (9-38) fails to correspond to measured distributions, then the entire argument must be examined step by step to locate the difficulty.

In practice the Maxwell velocity distribution has been checked in many ways and found to agree very well with experiment. We will sketch some general features of one type of measurement so as to make the argument more concrete. Suppose we have a vessel containing a gas and maintained at temperature $T$ as shown in Figure 9-2. If we place a hole in the vessel so that the rate of leak is small compared with the amount of gas in the vessel, we will not appreciably disturb the equilibrium. If we now place a slit in front of the hole and some distance from it, we should get through the slit a nearly parallel beam of molecules showing a Maxwell velocity distribution. This beam can now be passed through a device shown in Figure 9-3. Two concentric discs are rotated on a common axis. Each disc has a slit, the second slit being displaced by an angle $\delta$ from the first slit. The beam from the device in Figure 9-2 enters the analyzer from the left at $A$. Those molecules which pass through the first slit are undeviated, and in general hit the second disc. If the time of flight between the discs, $\tau$ is the time for the second disc to move an angular distance $\delta$, the molecules will pass through the second slit. This condition is

$$\tau = \frac{L}{v} = \frac{\delta}{\omega} \qquad (9\text{-}39)$$

The discs rotate at an angular velocity $\omega$, and $L$ is the distance between the discs. Particles will pass through both discs only if they have a velocity.

$$v = \frac{\omega L}{\delta} \qquad (9\text{-}40)$$

The angular velocity $\omega$ can be varied and the number of molecules coming through the second slit can be measured as a function of this quantity. The device then acts as a velocity spectrometer and can be used to analyze the beam coming from the apparatus in Figure 9-2.

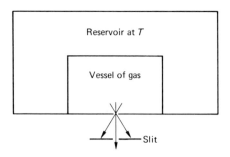

**Fig. 9-2.** Oven used to produce a stream of molecules to test the velocity distribution law.

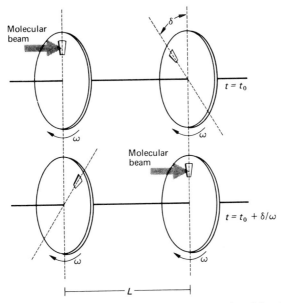

**Fig. 9-3.** Velocity spectrometer to analyze the beam produced by the device shown in Figure 9-2. The beam passes through two slits which are separated by a distance $L$ and are separated in time by $\delta/\omega$.

Such equipment has been used to directly measure the velocity distributions of gases which are found to conform to the Maxwell velocity distribution.

## F. INTERNAL DEGREES OF FREEDOM

The ability to relate the statistical approach to thermodynamics is not confined to ideal gases or to translational degrees of freedom. Internal degrees of freedom can be treated as well as a discussion of the interactions between molecules. The extension to internal degrees is relatively simple and we will discuss some examples. Molecular interactions are considerably more difficult to handle and we shall only be able to give a brief introduction into how the problem is treated.

For an individual molecule we can often write the energy as the sum of four terms:

$$\varepsilon_T = \varepsilon_t + \varepsilon_r + \varepsilon_v + \varepsilon_i \tag{9-41}$$

Equation (9-41) states that the total energy is the sum of the translational, rotational, vibrational, and interaction energies. It is an approximate relation and its validity must be examined for each case in which it is used. We will for the moment assume the equation and discuss how it can be used to include internal degrees of freedom in the analysis. First form the partition function corresponding to Equation (9-41):

$$Z = \sum e^{-\varepsilon_T/kT} = \sum_{t,r,v,i} e^{-(\varepsilon_t + \varepsilon_r + \varepsilon_v + \varepsilon_i)/kT}$$

$$= \sum_{t,r,v,i} e^{-\varepsilon_t/kT} e^{-\varepsilon_r/kT} e^{-\varepsilon_v/kT} e^{-\varepsilon_i/kT} \tag{9-42}$$

$$= \sum_t e^{-\varepsilon_t/kT} \sum_r e^{-\varepsilon_r/kT} \sum_v e^{-\varepsilon_v/kT} \sum_i e^{-\varepsilon_i/kT}$$

$$= Z_t Z_r Z_v Z_i$$

When the energy is in the form of Equation (9-42) the partition function is the product of four independent partition coefficients, one for each type of additive term. In going to the Helmholtz free energy for the system, we have

$$A = -kT \ln Z = -kT \ln Z_t Z_r Z_v Z_i \tag{9-43}$$

$$= -kT \ln Z_t - kT \ln Z_r - kT \ln Z_v - kT \ln Z_i$$

The partition functions for various internal degrees of freedom can thus be considered separately. For instance, for a diatomic molecule in a dilute gas we can write for its translational energy:

$$\varepsilon_t = \frac{n^2 h^2}{8mL^2} \tag{9-44}$$

Equation (9-44) comes from considering the molecule as a particle in a cubic box with sides of dimension $L$. The vibrational energies are also available from quantum mechanics. We can regard the molecule as a harmonic oscillator, two point masses connected by a spring (Figure 9-4). The solution to this problem, which we shall not carry out, is that

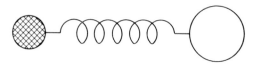

**Fig. 9-4.** Representation of a diatomic molecule as two masses connected by a spring.

the energy eigenvalues are

$$\varepsilon_v = \frac{h}{2\pi} \sqrt{\frac{K}{m}} \left( v + \frac{1}{2} \right) \tag{9-45}$$

$K$ is the spring constant (force constant in the molecular case), and $M$ is the reduced mass of the system and is equal to $m_A m_B / m_A + m_B$. The vibrational quantum number is $v$. Similarly, the molecule will have energy associated with its rotation about its center of gravity. The problem of the rigid rotator has also been solved in quantum mechanics, and the eigenvalues are

$$\varepsilon_r = \frac{r(r+1)h^2}{4\pi^2 I} \tag{9-46}$$

The quantity $I$ is the moment of inertia of the molecule computed about the center of mass and $r$ is the rotational quantum number.

It should be noted that Equations (9-45) and (9-46) can be derived in an exact way from the applications of the Schrödinger formulation of quantum mechanics. We are simply quoting the energy eigenvalues in order to indicate how real molecular situations are treated in statistical mechanics. In order to gain some more feeling for the method of approach, we shall proceed to show how one of the molecular partition functions can be computed from the energy eigenvalues.

The partition function for vibration can be formulated in the following way:

$$Z_v = \sum_{v=0}^{\infty} \exp \left[ -\frac{h}{2\pi} \sqrt{\frac{K}{m}} \left( v + \frac{1}{2} \right) \bigg/ kT \right] \tag{9-47}$$

Define a quantity $v$, the fundamental frequency of the oscillator

$$v = \frac{1}{2\pi} \sqrt{\frac{K}{m}} \tag{9-48}$$

This is the frequency of a classical oscillator of reduced mass $m$ and spring constant $K$. Define a second quantity $x$ as

$$x = e^{-hv/kT} \tag{9-49}$$

Equation (9-47) then becomes

$$Z_v = x^{1/2}[1 + x + x^2 + x^3 + x^4 + \cdots]$$
$$= \frac{x^{1/2}}{1-x} = \frac{e^{-hv/2kT}}{1 - e^{-hv/kT}} \tag{9-50}$$

The partition function for rotation can be computed by somewhat more elaborate processes. The resultant value is

$$Z_r = \frac{8\pi^2 I k T}{h^2} \tag{9-51}$$

The total partition function for noninteracting molecules then is

$$Z = \left[\frac{(2\pi m k T)^{3/2} V}{h^2}\right]\left[\frac{e^{-hv/2kT}}{1 - e^{-hv/kT}}\right]\left[\frac{8\pi^2 I k T}{h^2}\right] \tag{9-52}$$

Using Equation (9-52) we can now proceed to derive the thermodynamic quantities associated with internal degrees of freedom.

The problem of treating interactions between molecules is considerably more difficult since we can no longer consider partition functions of individual molecules but must consider the function for the whole collection of gases. Thus for a gas of $N$ molecules we could write

$$E = NE_T + N\left(\frac{\gamma N}{V}\right) \tag{9-53}$$

For the first term we sum up the internal terms from the $N$ individual molecules. The second term (applicable in the case of weak interactions only) asserts that the interaction energy for each molecule depends on the concentration of surrounding molecules. Treating actual cases depends on a study of the nature of $\gamma$.

The chief virtues of the methods we have been studying in this chapter is that we can utilize detailed analysis of molecules using the most precise available quantum-mechanical methods to describe and study the energetics and molecular mechanics. From the very best quantum-mechanical description of individual molecules and their interactions we can "explain" (predict) many thermodynamic properties of macroscopic collections of these molecules.

Very powerful applications have been made of these methods in biology. The helix-coil transition in DNA is perhaps one of the best examples of the important phenomena in biological macromolecules which have been treated with great insight by the methods of statistical thermodynamics. These techniques can be expected to add further understanding of biological macromolecules.

PROBLEMS

1. If a quantum-mechanical system has $W$ possible states and they all have the same energy $\varepsilon$ and there are no other possible states of the system, show that $S = k \ln W$.

2. Prove that the Helmholtz free energy is a state function.

3. What is the most probable value for the velocity of a perfect-gas molecule? Hint: Where does the maximum of $dp(v)/dv$ occur?

4. Discuss an example of the biological significance of the Maxwell velocity distribution.

# CHAPTER X

# Entropy, Information, and Energy

*"One if by land, two if by sea." Paul Revere
and his fellow citizens did not know information
theory, but they knew and utilized what is at the
basis of information theory, namely, the principle
of the representation of intelligence.*

HENRY QUASTLER in
"Symposium on Information
Theory in Biology"
Pergamon Press, 1958

## A. INFORMATION AND ENTROPY

The analytical form of the entropy function in statistical mechanics, as well as the approach used in our second method of deriving the distribution functions of statistical mechanics, suggests a relationship between entropy and information. Indeed, we may use the ensemble approach to provide a very direct link between the two concepts. Starting with an ensemble, let us serially number each member of the ensemble. The eigenfunction of each ensemble can be regarded as a symbol and the sequence of eigenfunctions constitutes a message in the sense indicated in our introduction to information theory. The probability of a system being in the $j$th eigenstate is $f_j$. We can then pose the question: What is the average information we would have if we knew which eigenstate a system was in? From Equation (7-17) of Chapter VII we can immediately write down the answer:

$$I = -\sum f_j \ln_2 f_j = -0.693 \sum f_j \ln f_j \qquad (10\text{-}1)$$

The numerical coefficient is introduced when the logarithm to the base two is converted to the logarithm to the base e.

The entropy of the ensemble just discussed is

$$S = -k \sum f_j \ln f_j \qquad (10\text{-}2)$$

Combining Equations (10-1) and (10-2) we get

$$S = \left(\frac{k}{0.693}\right) I \qquad (10\text{-}3)$$

The entropy is directly proportional to the information we would have if we knew which microstate the system was in. Entropy thus measures the amount of residual ignorance we have about the microstate of the system, once we know the equilibrium-state parameters. Note once more, entropy is related to the average information *we would have* if we had the maximal possible information about the detailed microscopic state of the system. Thus a system of high entropy is one in which a knowledge of the macroscopic state of the system tells very little as to which of the possible microstates it is in. Such a system is considered as disordered at the molecular level. However, order is used here in a somewhat subjective sense since the incompleteness is always in the observer's knowledge of which eigenstate a system is in. If we think of the phase-space representation, a high-entropy system is one whose representative point traverses a wide volume of phase space, while the phase point of a low-entropy system tends to be confined to a small subvolume of phase space. This point may be illustrated by our previous discussion of the entropy of mixing. Referring to Figure 10-1, suppose we have a molecule of $A$ in the left-hand box (the $X$ coordinate lying between 0 and 1) and a molecule of $B$ in the right-hand box (the $X$ coordinate lying between 1 and 2). Consider the phase point representing this system in coordinate space. Let the $X$ coordinate of the $A$ molecule be represented on the ordinate and the $X$ coordinate of the $B$ molecule be represented on the abscissa. Before mixing, the phase point is confined to the dashed square in Figure 10-2, while after mixing, the phase point can be anywhere within the larger square. The higher-entropy state after mixing gives us less knowledge about where the $A$ and $B$ molecules actually are.

Consider next the change of distribution of eigenstates with tem-

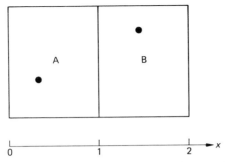

**Fig. 10-1.** Two boxes, of equal dimensions, one containing a molecule of *A* and the second containing a molecule of *B*.

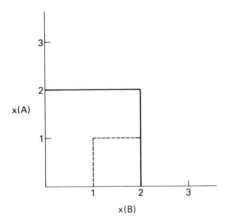

**Fig. 10-2.** The phase space corresponding to the *x* coordinates of molecules *A* and *B*. The portion enclosed by the dotted line is the available space before mixing, while the portion enclosed by the solid line is the space after mixing.

perature. We start by restating the distribution functions of statistical mechanics:

$$f_j = \frac{e^{-E_j/kT}}{\sum_{j=1}^{n} e^{-E_j/kT}} \tag{10-4}$$

The state numbered 1 is the lowest-lying eigenstate. As $T \to 0$, $f_1 \to 1$, $f_j \to 0$ for $j \neq 1$. At absolute zero the probability becomes one that the system will be found in the energetically lowest-lying eigenstate. The entropy in this case becomes

$$S = 1 \ln 1 + (n - 1)[0 \ln 0] = 0 \tag{10-5}$$

That is, since we know exactly what microstate the system is in, no further information remains to be obtained about the microstate and the entropy goes to zero.

The vanishing of the entropy at absolute zero had also been introduced on thermodynamic grounds alone and this postulate is known as the third law of thermodynamics. Statistical mechanics provides the basis for understanding this property of the entropy function.

In general, as a system goes from a state of higher entropy to a state of lower entropy, we go from a state of greater uncertainty about the microstate (high $I$) to a state of lesser uncertainty. We have gained information because in the second state we are less uncertain about the microscopic description of the system than we were orginally. Thus a decrease of entropy corresponds to an increase of information about the microstate. As a result of the preceding a good deal has been written about the equivalence of information and negentropy (entropy decrease). This has been somewhat confusing because from Equation (10-3) information measure and entropy are linearly related, so that a decrease of one is equivalent to a decrease of the other. The confusion is removed when we remember that entropy is proportional to a function which measures our lack of information about the microstate of a system. A high $I$ means that we would have a great deal of information *if* we knew which microstate a system was in, but this implies that we have very little knowledge as to which state it actually is in. As $I$ decreases ($S$ decreases) we are less unsure as to the state of the system, hence we have gained real information about the system. Therefore $-\Delta I$ represents the change in our information about the system, and a decrease of entropy does correspond to an increase in our actual knowledge about the microstate of the system. So negentropy is information, but this poetical form of the statement has to be thoroughly understood so as not to be confusing.

### B. Maxwell's Demon

The entropy of a system is also related to its capacity to do work, so that in some way information, which is a rather biological or even psychological concept, is related to purely energetic concepts. This problem was seen by Maxwell, who introduced an imaginary construct known as a Maxwell demon. The demon is located at a wall between two chambers of equal pressure of ideal gas, the entire system being embedded in an isothermal reservoir. This is seen in Figure 10-3. The

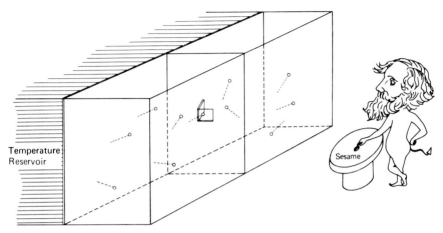

**Fig. 10-3.** A Maxwell demon controlling a door between two chambers each initially at temperature $T_1$, and pressure $P_1$.

demon operates a small trap door between the two chambers. Whenever he sees a molecule approaching the door from the right and no molecule approaching from the left, he opens the door. In time a pressure difference develops and work can be done by moving the wall and having it hooked up to an external mechanical device. The demon then opens the door, the wall is restored to its original position, and the demon begins his selection all over again. The entire device of the demon plus the gas reservoirs operates in a cycle and transfers heat from the reservoir into mechanical work, thus violating the second law of thermodynamics. If one accepts the validity of the second law, one must conclude that the demon cannot exist.

The reason for the apparent contradiction is that we have not examined the physical process by which the demon obtains information about molecules. Two approaches are available: one is to try to examine the details of the measurement to try to see what limitations are imposed, and the second is to assume the validity of the second law and see what limitations this imposes on the measuring process. We proceed with the second approach and consider two chambers of equal volume with a wall between them. A molecule is in one of the chambers but we do not know which one (Figure 10-4). The amount of information we have in determining which chamber the molecule is in is

$$I = -\ln_2 \tfrac{1}{2} = \ln_2 2 = 1 \text{ bit} \qquad (10\text{-}6)$$

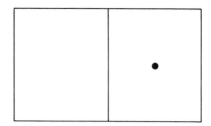

*Fig. 10-4.* Two chambers separated by a wall. One of the two chambers is occupied by a molecule.

The entropy decrease in knowing which side the molecule is on is the same as the entropy decrease in compressing a gas of original concentration $1/2V$ to a final concentration of $1/V$:

$$S = \frac{1}{T} \int_{2V}^{V} P \, dV = \frac{1}{T} \int_{2V}^{V} \frac{kT}{V} \, dV = -k \ln 2 \qquad (10\text{-}7)$$

Thus the determination of which side the molecule is on entails an entropy decrease of $-k \ln 2$. The measurement process must be accompanied by an entropy increase of at least $k \ln 2$ in order to preserve the second law.

An alternative view of the situation comes from the realization that knowing which side the molecule is on enables us to hook up the system to an external piston and do an amount of work $kT \ln 2$. Such a process could be repeated cyclically, violating the engine statement of the second law. Information about the microstate enables us to convert thermal energy into work.

Alternatively, Brillouin has shown that work must be expended to obtain information, so that the second law could be derived as a consequence of the theory of measurements. (See *Science and Information Theory*, by L. Brillouin, Academic Press, New York, 1960.)

The situation can be summarized as follows. One of the most fundamental properties of matter on a macroscopic scale is temperature. At a molecular level temperature manifests itself as the kinetic energy of atoms and molecules. Compared to a human observer, molecules are very small, very numerous, and interact very rapidly. These interactions lead to continuous energy exchange between the particles of the system. From a macroscopic point of view we therefore describe the energy as being randomly distributed among the possible degrees of freedom. The Maxwell–Boltzmann distribution function enables us to state the statistical distribution. Indeed, it is possible to prove that there is an average energy of $\frac{1}{2}kT$ associated with each degree of freedom which contributes an energy term proportional to the square of the parameter (such as $v_x{}^2$, $v_y{}^2$, $v_z{}^2$). To convert all of this kinetic energy to work requires a detailed knowledge of each molecule so that it can be hooked up to an external work device. If this knowledge were available, we could continuously convert heat to work. Obtaining detailed molecular knowledge requires measurements, and performing a measurement requires the expenditure of energy (you don't get something for nothing—even information). Hence an entropic price has to be paid to get work out of a heat source.

The preceding considerations are of minor importance in classical thermodynamics, where one deals with large systems and gross macroscopic properties. They become of greater importance when small systems and nonequilibrium systems are considered. They become of very great importance in dealing with a small, highly organized, far from equilibrium system such as a living cell.

The relation between entropy, information, and work thus appears to involve some unusual concepts. Entropy and information about microstates are rather equivalent. Entropy relates the measure to the system and information relates the measure to the observer. This is, however, a rather artificial distinction since thermodynamics always implies the observer as establishing or removing constraints on the system or otherwise manipulating. Microscopic information can also be converted into work and the conversion factor is temperature, the amount of energy stored in microscopic kinetic modes. Alternatively, work can be converted into information since one can do work to place a system in a certain microstate or at least a group of microstates considerably more restricted than the equilibrium ensemble. Continuous work can therefore lead to the self-organization of systems, and this is the principle which underlies the ordering of the biosphere.

PROBLEMS

1. A volume of 22.4 liters containing one mole of perfect gas and in contact with a reservoir at 300°C is reduced to one liter.
   (a) What is the increase of information?
   (b) How may this information be converted to work and how much work is available?

    (c)   What is the maximum amount of work that can be extracted from the liter of gas?

2. Design and analyze a device to violate the second law of thermo-dynamics.

3. A bullet hits a stationary wall and volatilizes. Analyze the loss of molecular information accompanying the process.

4. A group of $N$ birds is randomly circling around at average velocity $v$. Suddenly they all start to fly south (within $\pm 1°$) at average velocity $v$. Calculate the change of entropy.

5. Starting from Equation (10-4), show that as $T \to 0$, $f_1 \to 1$ and $f_j \to 0$ for all other values of $j$.

CHAPTER **XI**

# Free-Energy Functions

*The leading ideas which I followed in my paper on the Equilibrium of Heterogeneous Substances was to develop the roles of energy and entropy in the theory of thermo-dynamic equilibrium. By means of these quantities the general condition of equilibrium is easily expressed, and by applying this to various cases we are led at once to the special conditions which characterize them.*

J. WILLARD GIBBS,
in a letter to the American
Academy of Arts and Sciences,
January, 10, 1881

## A. GIBBS FREE ENERGY

Our primary concern in this chapter is developing the apparatus which underlies the application of thermodynamics to actual problems in chemistry and biochemistry. For that reason our approach will be somewhat less general as we shift to defining standard states and otherwise developing conventions for use with real systems. Working out these details burdens this chapter with somewhat more than its share of algebraic tedium. It seems a price worth paying for deeper understanding of what is actually done in the use of thermodynamics.

As we have already indicated, the most general description of the equilibrium of a system is that state which maximizes the entropy of the universe, which is interpreted as system plus surroundings. The entropy of the universe is, however, often a difficult quantity to measure and sometimes beset with conceptual difficulties. It is usually possible under restricted conditions to find functions of the state of the system only which can be related to the global entropy. The most often used of these functions are given special names and form important tools in solving thermodynamic problems. The formulation of these functions will be discussed by considering a number of equilibrium situations.

First, we discuss a closed system at constant pressure and constant temperature. At equilibrium the entropy is a maximum, so that infinitesimal changes at equilibrium correspond to the mathematical condition

$$dS_u = 0 \qquad (11\text{-}1)$$

The quantity $dS_u$ is the entropy change of the universe and may be split into two parts, $dS_s$, the entropy change of the system, and $dS_r$, the entropy change of the rest of the universe. Equation (11-1) can then be written

$$dS_u = dS_s + dS_r = 0 \qquad (11\text{-}2)$$

A system at constant pressure and temperature interacts with the outside world by being in contact with an isothermal reservoir through a diathermal wall and being in contact with an isobaric reservoir through an adiabatic wall. Therefore $dS_r$ can only result from the passage of an amount of heat $dQ$ across the diathermal wall. If $dQ_s$ is the amount of heat change in the system, the heat change of the reservoir is $-dQ_s$ and the entropy change of the reservoir is $-dQ_s/T$. For the system we can write the first law of thermodynamics

$$dQ_s = dU_s + P\,dV \qquad (11\text{-}3)$$

Equations (11-2) and (11-3) can then be combined in the following way:

$$dS_u = dS_s - \frac{dQ_s}{T} = dS_s - \frac{dU_s}{T} - \frac{P\,dV}{T} = 0 \qquad (11\text{-}4)$$

The condition of equilibrium is now expressed entirely in terms of system parameters $S_s$, $U_s$, $T$, $P$, $V$. Equation (11-4) may be rewritten

$$T\,dS_s - dU_s - P\,dV = 0 \qquad (11\text{-}5)$$

The condition expressed by this equation indicates that there is some function of the system alone which has an extremum at equilibrium, which extremum is equivalent to maximizing the entropy of the universe. We choose a function which we designate $G$ which fulfills these conditions:

$$G = U + PV - TS \qquad (11\text{-}6)$$

If we now proceed to take the differential of $G$ and apply the isothermal and isobaric conditions $dT = 0$, $dP = 0$, Equation (11-6) reduces to

$$dG = dU + P\,dV - T\,dS \qquad (11\text{-}7)$$

Comparison of Equations (11-7) and ((11-5) indicates that the condition $-dG = 0$ is equivalent to the entropy maximization. The condition of equilibrium can then be expressed as the minimum value of $G$ (maximum value of $-G$). $G$ is called the Gibbs free energy and plays a leading role in the biological and biochemical applications of thermodynamics owing to the fact that many reactions take place at constant pressure (atmospheric) and constant temperature (either ambient or subject to temperature homeostatis in the case of higher organisms).

## B. HELMHOLTZ FREE ENERGY

For systems at constant temperature and constant volume a function of the system other than $G$ is appropriate to describe the equilibrium condition. Equations (11-1) and (11-2) still apply as the most general condition of equilibrium. However, imposing the condition of constant volume modifies Equation (11-3) so that the $P\,dV$ term drops out on the right-hand side, leading to the change in internal energy being equal to the heat term. The equilibrium equations [analogous to (11-4) and (11-5)] now become

$$dS_{\mathrm{u}} = dS_{\mathrm{s}} - \frac{dQ_{\mathrm{s}}}{T} = dS_{\mathrm{s}} - \frac{dU_{\mathrm{s}}}{T} = 0 \qquad (11\text{-}8)$$

Equation (11-8) may be rewritten as

$$T\,dS_{\mathrm{s}} - dU_{\mathrm{s}} = 0 \qquad (11\text{-}9)$$

Equation (11-9) corresponds to the minimum of a new function $A$ which may be written

$$A = U - TS \qquad (11\text{-}10)$$

*A* is called the Helmholtz free energy and has already been introduced in Chapter IX [Equation (9-22)] as the function relating the partition function to thermodynamics. Its significance here is that it is a function of the state of the system only whose minimum corresponds to maximum entropy of the universe under conditions of constant temperature and volume.

In addition to the Gibbs and Helmholtz free energies, another energy function of interest is defined and designated as the enthalpy *H*,

$$H = U + PV \tag{11-11}$$

Referring back to Equation (11-6), we can relate the enthalpy and Gibbs free energy

$$G = H - TS \tag{11-12}$$

To sum up, we note that utilizing the fundamental thermodynamic quantities $U$, $T$, $S$, $P$, and $V$ we can build up a series of functions which are particularly useful in special applications. The Gibbs free energy has the virtue of being a minimum at equilibrium under the usual conditions for biochemical experiments. The Helmholtz free energy is a minimum under constant-volume isothermal conditions and more importantly is directly available from the partition function of statistical mechanics. The enthalpy function, as we shall shortly see, allows the direct relation between thermochemical data and thermodynamic functions.

## C. GENERALIZED ENERGY FUNCTION

The full meaning of the various free-energy functions only becomes manifest when we know $U$ as a function of the parameters of state or, in the more general case, when we know $dU$. With the exception of very idealized cases, such as perfect gases, the functional relation between $U$ and the rest of the state parameters is hardly ever known. The changes in total energy $dU$ can, however, be appreciably generalized. We have previously formulated $dU$ as

$$dU = dQ - P\,dV + \sum_i \mu_i\,dn_i \tag{11-13}$$

The right-hand side refers to ways in which energy can enter or leave the system. The equation may be extended as follows:

$$dU = dQ - P\,dV + \sum \mu_i\,dn_i + \mathscr{E}\,de$$
$$+ \mathscr{G}\,dm + \sigma\,d\mathscr{A} + \mathscr{T}\,dl + \mathscr{H}\,d\mathscr{M} \tag{11-14}$$

The term $\mathscr{E}\,de$ refers to the energy change of the system due to the flow of an amount of charge $de$ driven by an applied potential $\mathscr{E}$. Equations derived from the introduction of this term form the basis of electrochemistry. The term $\mathscr{G}\,dm$ is the change of gravitational energy due to the increase of mass of the system $dm$ in a gravitational potential $\mathscr{G}$. The gravitational potential may be nonuniform within a system, in which case the energy may be changed by altering the position of a mass $m$ in the gravitational field. The term that would then be used would be

$$m\,d\mathscr{G} = m\,\frac{d\mathscr{G}(x)}{dx}\,dx$$

The use of this type of external mechanical force is of importance in deriving the equations of equilibrium ultracentrifugation and also in meteorological problems involving the earth's atmosphere.

If $\sigma$ is the surface energy or surface tension and $d\mathscr{A}$ the change in surface area, then $\sigma\,d\mathscr{A}$ is the change in energy due to extending surfaces. In systems of high surface-to-volume ratio this energy can be an appreciable part of the total energy. The $\sigma\,d\mathscr{A}$ term turns out to be of importance in studying the surface adsorption of molecules.

$\mathscr{T}\,dl$ is a tension elongation term and refers to linear structures in the system, which may be wires, rubber bands, or extensible linear macromolecules. It is a one-dimensional analog of the $P\,dV$ term, tension playing the role of pressure and extension $dl$ playing the role of volume change.

The application of an external magnetic field $\mathscr{H}$ can also alter the energy of a system. If $d\mathscr{M}$ is the change in the degree of magnetization, this energy is expressed as $\mathscr{H}\,d\mathscr{M}$.

Equation (11-14) is of course open-ended and any number of additional energy terms may be added. This equation forms the starting point for much of the actual analysis of thermodynamics and those terms on the right-side are chosen that are pertinent to the problem being studied. For straightforward homogeneous phase chemical thermodynamics, Equation (11-13) provides a suitable starting point. Our first aim is to study the energy changes accompanying chemical reactions taking place at constant temperature and pressure. If we combine Equations (11-13) and (11-7) and use the fact that for reversible transformations $dQ = T\,dS$, we then get the result that at constant temperature and pressure

$$dG = \sum \mu_i\,dn_i \qquad (11\text{-}15)$$

At equilibrium $dG$ equals zero since $G$ must be an extremum, and we have the following relation:

$$\sum \mu_i \, dn_i = 0 \tag{11-16}$$

This equation describes the thermodynamic conditions for chemical equilibrium and indicates how the infinitesimal changes in the equilibrium amount of various chemical species must be related.

Consider a chemical reaction in which a group of reactants are converted into products. The change of Gibbs free energy for the process is the integral of $dG$ from the initial state to the final state. If there is a reversible pathway from reactants to products such that each state is an equilibrium state, then at constant temperature and pressure we have

$$\Delta G = \int_{\text{initial}}^{\text{final}} dG = 0 \tag{11-17}$$

The previous equation holds since $dG = 0$ everywhere along the path. However, since $G$ is a function of state, $\Delta G$ will have the same value for all paths from the same initial to the same final state. Chemical reactions being carried out reversibly at constant temperature and pressure therefore take place at constant $G$.

## D. ENTHALPY AND STANDARD STATES

Consider next the change in enthalpy in processes taking place at constant temperature and pressure. Starting with Equations (11-11) and (11-13), we get

$$dH = dU + PdV + V\,dP = dQ - P\,dV + \sum \mu_i \, dn_i + PdV + V\,dP \tag{11-18}$$

Introducing the restriction of constant pressure, $dP = 0$, and using Equation (11-15), we then get

$$dH = dQ + dG \tag{11-19}$$

For a chemical reaction going from reactants to products we have

$$\Delta H = \int_{\text{initial}}^{\text{final}} dH = \int_{\text{initial}}^{\text{final}} dQ + \int_{\text{initial}}^{\text{final}} dG \tag{11-20}$$

The first term on the right is the total heat transferred to the reservoir $\Delta Q$, while the second term is $\Delta G$, which we have just shown to be zero under these conditions. Equation (11-20) then reduces to

$$\Delta H = \Delta Q \tag{11-21}$$

$\Delta Q$ can be measured by allowing the reaction to take place in a calorimeter (see Chapter XIV). Equation (11-21) thus provides us with a state function, the enthalpy whose changes can be measured by direct calorimetry. $\Delta H$ for a specific reaction is called the heat of the reaction. In specifying the value of $\Delta H$ it is necessary not only to enumerate the reactants and products, but to specify what state they are in, as $\Delta H$, being the difference of two state functions, clearly depends on the detailed nature of the initial and final states. Thus a given chemical reaction has in principle an infinite number of heats of reaction depending on what the initial and final states actually are. To obviate this difficulty and to provide for tabular data, a series of standard states is defined and all standard data (handbook values) are given relative to these standard states. The present conventions are as follows:

(a) The standard temperature is chosen as 25°C. For pure substances $dH = dQ = C_p \, dT$. Thus if we wish to calculate enthalpies at any other temperature, we can integrate $dH$ from the standard temperature to the second temperature. This requires that we know the value of $C_p$ as a function of $T$ over the desired temperature range.

(b) The standard state of a solid is its most stable form at 25°C and 1 atm pressure unless otherwise specified. For carbon the standard state is chosen to be graphite. The choice could have just as well been diamond (it was in some of the earlier work) and the enthalpy values obtained would vary by the enthalpy difference between graphite and diamond.

(c) The standard state of a liquid is the most stable form at 25°C and 1 atm pressure.

(d) Two standard states may be used for gases: (1) One atmosphere pressure at 25°C; (2) pressure approaching zero at 25°C.

(e) For exothermic reactions $\Delta H$ is negative.

The preceding establishes the basis for thermochemistry. The combustion of carbon provides an example:

$$C + O_2 \rightleftharpoons CO_2, \qquad \Delta H_0 = -94.0518 \quad \text{Kcal/mole} \qquad (11\text{-}22)$$

Thus one mole of graphite at 1 atm pressure and 25°C combusts with one mole of oxygen gas at 25° and 1 atm pressure to give one mole of $CO_2$ at 25° and 1 atm pressure. The heat given up to a calorimeter is $-94.0518$ Kcal/mole.

The fact that enthalpy is a state function means that enthalpy changes in successive reactions are additive; that is, for the same reactants and products the enthalpy change will be the same regardless of the intermediate pathways. This relationship was established empirically before it was formulated on thermodynamic grounds and was known as Hess's law of constant heat summation. As an example, consider the previous combustion of graphite and allow it to take place in two steps:

$$C + \tfrac{1}{2}O_2 \rightleftharpoons CO, \qquad \Delta H_1 = -26.4157 \quad \text{Kcal/mole} \quad (11\text{-}23)$$

$$CO + \tfrac{1}{2}O_2 \rightleftharpoons CO_2, \qquad \Delta H_2 = -67.6361 \quad \text{Kcal/mole} \quad (11\text{-}24)$$

The previous discussion indicates that the overall $\Delta H$ in going from graphite and $O_2$ to $CO_2$ is the sum of the two intermediate steps, so that the sum of $\Delta H_1$ and $\Delta H_2$ is $-94.0518$ Kcal/mole, which is of course equal to the $\Delta H$ of the overall reaction as indicated in Equation (11-22). The summation rule is useful in cases where one reaction in a sequence cannot be isolated. Suppose, for instance, that we could carry out the calorimetry on reactions shown in equations (11-22) and (11-23) but we were unable to run a controlled reaction (11-24) for calorimetry. We could still determine $\Delta H_2$ as $\Delta H_0 - \Delta H_1$. In many cases this type of determination proves to be of importance.

## E. THE EULER EQUATION

To develop the properties of the free-energy functions further, we need to explore one further property of the internal energy $U$. We have already noted that for simple systems $U$ may be expressed as a function of the volume, entropy and mole numbers:

$$U = U(S, V, n_i) \tag{11-25}$$

Consider two such identical systems and bring them together. The volume, entropy, and mole numbers will double and so will the energy. This argument can be extended and put in the following mathematical form:

$$U(\lambda S, \lambda V, \lambda n_i) = \lambda U(S, V, n_i) \tag{11-26}$$

Stated verbally, Equation (11-26) says that if a system is uniformly enlarged (or shrunk) by a factor $\lambda$, so that the entropy, volume, and all mole numbers change by a factor $\lambda$, then the internal energy will also change by a factor $\lambda$. This is a rather obvious additivity property which can be deduced from our previous discussions of the various parameters. Equation (11-26) allows us to formulate the energy functions in very useful ways. If we differentiate Equation (11-26) with respect to $\lambda$, we get

$$\frac{\partial U}{\partial(\lambda S)}\frac{\partial(\lambda S)}{\partial \lambda} + \frac{\partial U}{\partial(\lambda V)}\frac{\partial(\lambda V)}{\partial \lambda} + \sum \frac{\partial U}{\partial(\lambda n_i)}\frac{d(\lambda n_i)}{\partial \lambda} = U(S, V, n_i) \qquad (11\text{-}27)$$

Carrying out the differentiation of the second term in each pair, the equation may be rewritten

$$\frac{\partial U}{\partial(\lambda S)} S + \frac{\partial U}{\partial(\lambda V)} V + \sum \frac{\partial U}{\partial(\lambda n_i)} n_i = U \qquad (11\text{-}28)$$

The parameter $\lambda$ is arbitrary and can take on any value. In particular, for $\lambda = 1$, Equation (11-28) becomes

$$\frac{\partial U}{\partial S} S + \frac{\partial U}{\partial V} V + \sum \frac{\partial U}{\partial n_i} n_i = U \qquad (11\text{-}29)$$

But we have already shown that

$$\frac{\partial U}{\partial S} = T, \qquad \frac{\partial U}{\partial V} = -P, \qquad \frac{\partial U}{\partial n_i} = \mu_i \qquad (11\text{-}30)$$

Hence Equation (11-30) becomes

$$U = TS - PV + \sum \mu_i n_i \qquad (11\text{-}31)$$

The additivity property has allowed us to integrate the internal energy. If we combine Equation (11-31) with Equation (11-6), we see that

$$G = \sum \mu_i n_i \qquad (11\text{-}32)$$

The Gibbs free energy can thus be formulated solely as a function of the chemical potentials and mole numbers. In particular for one mole of a pure substance in its standard state we may write

$$G_{i0} = \mu_{i0} \qquad (11\text{-}33)$$

The particularly simple forms of Equations (11-32) and (11-33) are of great value in the applications of thermodynamics to chemical equilibrium, and stress the utility of the choice of Gibbs free energy in handling such problems.

Equation (11-32) may be arrived at in a way which is mathematically less elegant but carries more physical intuition. If we go back to Equation (11-15), which holds at constant temperature and pressure, we see that $G$ can be determined if we have a path of integration. Consider a system whose concentration, temperature, and pressure are kept constant, but whose various components are added in fixed ratios,

$$dn_i = n_{i(\text{final})}\, d\xi \tag{11-34}$$

Equation (11-34) implies that we build up the system by the simultaneous addition of all the components in fixed ratios. While this may seem unusual, it is physically possible and therefore provides a legitimate pathway and allows us to integrate Equation (11-15). Because the $\mu_i$ are intensive variables, they are independent of the total size of the system and will depend only on the concentrations, pressure, and temperature. Thus the $\mu_i$ are constant during the integration and the only variable along the path is $\xi$:

$$dG = \sum n_{i(\text{final})} \mu_i\, d\xi \tag{11-35}$$

and

$$G = \int_0^1 \sum n_{i(\text{final})} \mu_i\, d\xi = \sum n_{i(\text{final})} \mu_i \int_0^1 d\xi \tag{11-36}$$

$$= \sum n_{i(\text{final})} \mu_i$$

The Gibbs free energy function is thus found to be the same by the two methods of determination. Equation (11-36) states that the Gibbs free energy of a system is the sum of the products of the molar chemical potential of each substance times the number of moles of that substance. Starting with Equation (11-36), we can restate the equilibrium conditions,

$$dG = \sum \mu_i\, dn_i + \sum n_i\, d\mu_i = 0 \tag{11-37}$$

But because of Equation (11-15) we can then write

$$\sum n_i\, d\mu_i = 0 \tag{11-38}$$

Equation (11-38) is known as the Gibbs–Duhem relation and is a useful device in solving problems of chemical thermodynamics. Equations (11-15), (11-37), and (11-38) all describe chemical equilibrium, and the different forms are useful in different problems.

F. ACTIVITY

The molar chemical potential $\mu$ is often a difficult quantity to determine, and a related quantity, the activity, is frequently used. The activity of the $i$th substance $a_i$ is defined by the following relation:

$$a_i = e^{(\mu_i - \mu_{i0})/RT} \quad \text{(definition)} \tag{11-39}$$

$\mu_{i0}$ is the chemical potential of the $i$th substance in the standard state; $R$ is the gas constant and $T$ the temperature. Equation (11-39) is more usually written as

$$RT \ln a_i = \mu_i - \mu_{i0} \tag{11-40}$$

The activity concept does not adapt itself to any simple intuitive interpretation. The right-hand side of Equation (11-40) represents the energy difference in taking one mole of the $i$th substance from its standard state to the state under consideration. Dividing $\mu_i - \mu_{i0}$ by $RT$ gives a ratio of the energy change to the thermal energy. In general, activity measures the reactivity of the $i$th substance. By appropriate choice of standard states the activity can be made numerically equal to the concentration of dilute solutions. Note, however, that the activity is a dimensionless quantity, since the logarithm is equal to the ratio of two energies.

Utilizing the activity concept makes possible a detailed thermodynamic study of equilibrium in chemical reactions. A generalized chemical reaction can be written

$$aA + bB \rightleftharpoons cC + dD \tag{11-41}$$

The lowercase letters designate the stoichiometric coefficients, while the capitals designate the substances: thus $a$ moles of A react with $b$ moles of B to give $c$ moles of C and $d$ moles of D. The two arrows indicate that the reaction is reversible; that is, we can start with C and D and make A and B. Theoretically, all reactions are reversible in this sense, although there are often great practical difficulties in realizing this reversibility. An even more general representation of chemical reactions is given below:

$$\sum v_k x_k \rightleftharpoons \sum v_j x_j \tag{11-42}$$

The $v$'s are stoichiometric coefficients, the $k$-subscripts represent reactants, and the $j$'s represent products. At equilibrium at constant temperature and pressure we have that for any infinitesimal changes in the $n_i$

$$dG = \sum \mu_i \, dn_i = 0 \tag{11-43}$$

Small fluctuations in $n_i$ at equilibrium are not, however, independent, owing to the stoichiometric constraints [Equation (11-42)], so that each

$dn_i$ must be represented by

$$dn_i = v_i \, d\xi \tag{11-44}$$

where $v_k$ are assigned negative coefficients and $v_j$ are assigned positive ones. The quantity $\xi$ is usually designated the extent of the reaction or the degree of advancement. We next substitute Equations (11-40) and (11-44) into (11-43). This yields

$$\sum (RT \ln a_i + \mu_{i0}) v_i \, d\xi = 0 \tag{11-45}$$

Equation (11-45) is a general expression for equilibrium in terms of activities as independent variables. Since $d\xi$ is arbitrary, Equation (11-45) requires the vanishing of its coefficient. This leads to

$$-\sum_k (RT \ln a_i + \mu_{i0}) v_i + \sum_j (RT \ln a_i + \mu_{i0}) v_i = 0 \tag{11-46}$$

Equation (11-46) can be rearranged putting all the activity terms on the left-hand side and all the standard-state chemical potential terms on the right-hand side. We use the mathematical fact that the sum of logarithms is equal to the logarithm of the product and we employ the notation of $\prod_i$ representing a sequential product. We may then write

$$RT \ln \frac{\prod_j a_i^{v_i}}{\prod_k a_i^{v_i}} = \sum_k \mu_{i0} v_i - \sum_j \mu_{i0} v_i a \tag{11-47}$$

The right-hand side now represents the standard-state Gibbs free energy of the reactants minus the standard-state free energy of the products, and is designated $-\Delta G_0$. It is the difference in free energy between reactants and products if all components were in their standard states. Equation (11-47) can be rewritten as

$$\frac{\prod_j a_i^{v_i}}{\prod_k a_i^{v_i}} = e^{-\Delta G_0 / RT} \tag{11-48}$$

For the specific reaction shown in Equation (11-41), the equilibrium condition can be expressed as

$$\frac{a_C{}^c a_D{}^d}{a_A{}^a a_B{}^b} = e^{-\Delta G_0 / RT} \tag{11-49}$$

The right-hand side is often designated the equilibrium constant, represented by the letter $K$,

$$e^{-\Delta G_0 / RT} = K \tag{11-50}$$

Equations (11-48) and (11-49) look very similar to the mass-action law except that activities appear on the left side rather than concentrations. Equation (11-49) is the true thermodynamic form of the chemical equilibrium and equations using concentration are in fact merely approximations. As noted, activities are, however very different from concentrations, and are defined solely by Equation (11-44) or (11-45), along with the specification of standard states.

As already stated, when the proper choice of standard states is made it is often possible to replace activities by concentrations or mole fractions or some other experimentally accessible quantities. In order to gain an understanding of why such approximations can be made [which is not at all obvious from the defining relation of Equation (11-39)], we must actually work through some detailed examples. This is well worth the effort, as activities are often treated in a rather mystical fashion and only by working our way through actual cases can we clear away this aura of mystery.

We will first examine the case of a mixture of two perfect gases in a volume $V$ containing $n_1$ moles of the first and $n_2$ moles of the second. We then have

$$U = \tfrac{3}{2} n_1 RT + \tfrac{3}{2} n_2 RT = \tfrac{3}{2} RT(n_1 + n_2) \qquad (11\text{-}51)$$

The entropy of the system is the entropy of each component [Equation (A5-5), Appendix III] plus the entropy of mixing [Equation (6-32), Chapter VI]. We first write the entropy of a single component of perfect gas. This is derived in Appendix III and shown to be

$$S = \tfrac{3}{2} R \ln T + R \ln V + B \qquad (11\text{-}52)$$

For the volume of one mole we can replace $V$ by $RT/P$. We make this substitution into Equation (11-52) and define a new constant $B'$ which is $B + R \ln R$. The resultant form of the entropy function is

$$S = \tfrac{5}{2} R \ln T - R \ln P + B' \qquad (11\text{-}53)$$

If we now take $n_1$ moles of the first gas at pressure $P$ and $n_2$ moles of the second gas at pressure $P$ and mix them (the final pressure is $P$), then the entropy consists of the contribution of each component plus the entropy of mixing,

$$
\begin{aligned}
S = \tfrac{5}{2} n_1 R \ln T &- n_1 R \ln P + n_1 B' \\
+ \tfrac{5}{2} n_2 R \ln T &- n_2 R \ln P + n_2 B' \\
- R \Big( n_1 \ln \frac{n_1}{n_1 + n_2} &+ n_2 \ln \frac{n_2}{n_1 + n_2} \Big)
\end{aligned}
\qquad (11\text{-}54)
$$

The Gibbs free energy of the system $G$ is $U + PV - TS$. We can then use Equations (11-51) and (11-54) to eliminate $U$ and $S$ and get $G$ as a function of the $n_i$. In getting the appropriate form of the equation, we substitute $(n_1 + n_2)RT$ for $PV$ and use the definition of the mole fraction of the $i$th substance $N_i$, being equal to $n_i$ divided by the sum of the $n_i$. This leads to

$$G = \tfrac{5}{2}n_1 RT - \tfrac{5}{2}n_1 RT \ln T + n_1 RT \ln P - n_1 B_1'T + n_1 RT \ln N_1$$
$$+ \tfrac{5}{2}n_2 RT - \tfrac{5}{2}n_2 RT \ln T + n_2 RT \ln P - n_2 B_2'T + n_2 RT \ln N_2$$

$$(11\text{-}55)$$

We now define a new quantity $f_i(T)$, which is a function of temperature only,

$$f_i(T) = \tfrac{5}{2}RT - \tfrac{5}{2}RT \ln T + B_i'T \tag{11-56}$$

Using this newly defined quantity, we can rewrite Equation (11-55) in the following much simpler form:

$$G = \sum_{i=1,2} n_i[RT \ln N_i + RT \ln P + f_i(T)] \tag{11-57}$$

Equation (11-57) may be generalized to any number of perfect-gas components. The form of the equation is suggestive of the integrated form of the free energy in Equation (11-32) ($G = \sum_i \mu_i n_i$) and comparison of the two allows us to write down the detailed expression for the chemical potential

$$\mu_i = RT \ln N_i + RT \ln P + f_i(T) \tag{11-58}$$

The next steps involve some algebraic manipulation in order to express $\mu$ as a function of the concentration $C_i$, which is by definition $n_i/V$. The mole fraction $N_i$ can therefore be rewritten as $C_i V/\sum n_i$. If we substitute these values in Equation (11-58) and rearrange terms, we get

$$\mu_i = RT \ln C_i + RT \ln \frac{PV}{\sum n_i} + f_i(T) \tag{11-59}$$

The quantity $PV/\sum n_i$ is just $RT$, so we reduce expression (11-59) to

$$\mu_i = RT \ln C_i + RT \ln RT + f_i(T) \tag{11-60}$$

Our definition of activity in Equation (11-40) allows us to set $\mu_i$ in Equation (11-60) equal to $\mu_{i0} + RT \ln a_i$ and we proceed with this substitution:

$$RT \ln a_i + \mu_0 = RT \ln C_i + RT \ln RT + f_i(T) \tag{11-61}$$

We are now free to choose a standard state, which we will pick as 25°C (we call this $T_0$) and a concentration of one mole per liter. In the standard state the activity is unity since $\mu_i = \mu_{i0}$ for this condition. Therefore, since ln 1 is equal to zero, we get

$$\mu_0 = RT_0 \ln RT_0 + f_i T_0 \tag{11-62}$$

From Equation (11-61) and (11-62) we can see that $a_i$ is equal to $C_i$. It should be noted that the equating of $a_i$ and $C_i$ requires a fairly elaborate argument and depends both on the choice of standard state and the units in which $C_i$ is expressed (moles per liter in the present example).

In general for ideal mixtures it is possible to choose a standard state so that the activity and concentration approach each other over some range of variables. It is instructive to examine one more case, that of ideal solutions. Start with $n_1$ moles of component 1 and $n_2$ moles of component 2, each in the pure state. Mix the two components at constant temperature and pressure. From the definition of $G$ and the boundary conditions, we see

$$\Delta G = \Delta H - T \Delta S \tag{11-63}$$

Ideal solutions are characterized by $\Delta H = 0$, no heat of mixing, and the only entropy change being the entropy of mixing. Thus, before mixing, the Gibbs free energy of the system can be expressed as

$$G_0 = \sum_i n_{i0} \mu_{i0} \tag{11-64}$$

This equation assumes all components are in their standard state. After mixing, we can write

$$G = G_0 + \Delta G = \sum n_i \mu_{i0} + \sum n_i RT \ln \frac{n_i}{\sum n_i} \tag{11-65}$$

If we now utilize the fact that $G$ is the sum of $\mu_i n_i$, we can write for each chemical potential

$$\mu_i = \mu_{i0} + RT \ln N_i \tag{11-66}$$

The definition of activity allows us to set $a_i$ equal to $N_i$, the mole fraction. This approximation is frequently used for systems showing nearly ideal behavior. If we wish to write Equation (11-66) in terms of concentration, we substitute $C_i V$ for $n_i$ as in the previous example. This leads to

$$\mu_i = \mu_{i0} + RT \ln C_i + RT \ln \frac{V}{\sum n_i} \tag{11-67}$$

If we consider a two-component system and allow the solute $C_i$ to go to infinite dilution, the term $V/\sum n_i$ becomes $\bar{V}$, the partial molar volume of the solvent. If we now define a new $\mu_{io}$ equal to $\mu_{io} + RT \ln \bar{V}$, then we can once again set $a_i$ equal to $C_i$. Since a large number of substances approach ideal behavior at infinite dilution, this approach is quite general.

Having adopted standard states so as to equate activities with concentrations for ideal behavior, deviations from ideality are then lumped into an activity coefficient. We write

$$a_i = \gamma_i C_i \qquad (11\text{-}68)$$

The quantity $\gamma_i$ in general may be a function of concentration. Equation (11-68) preserves the simple form of the relation between activity and concentration but allows more complex situations to be treated.

### G. The Use of Alternative Methods

The chemical potential and the associated concept of the activity provide a method for solving a wide variety of problems. We will use it to solve a classical problem of pressure distribution in the atmosphere. We will then solve the same problem by statistical mechanics and finally by hydrostatics in an effort to see the relation between the different approaches. The problem is to find the density or pressure as a function of height for a column of perfect gas of unit area, constant temperature $T$, and pressure $P_a$ at the bottom of the column. The Gibbs free energy is a function of height if we introduce the gravitational potential as well as the chemical potential. Returning to Equation (11-14), we note

$$dU = dQ - P \, dV + \sum \mu_i \, dn_i + Mg \, dy \qquad (11\text{-}69)$$

Divide the column into slabs of thickness $dy$ (Figure 11-1). In order for the Gibbs free energy to be a minimum, the molar free energy must be the same for each slab, for if this were not true, molecules would move from slabs of high free energy to slabs of low free energy. Since we deal with a one-component system, we can write

$$G_i = \mu_i + M_i gy \qquad (11\text{-}70)$$

The molar free energy at any height is the sum of the chemical potential and the gravitational potential. $M_i$ is the mass per mole or the molecular weight of the $i$th substance. The gravitational acceleration is given by $g$ and the equilibrium condition for the total free energy to be a minimum

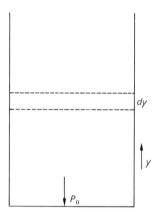

**Fig. 11-1.** Standing isothermal column of gas with the pressure $P_0$ at the bottom of the column. Column may be divided into layers of thickness $dy$.

is given by

$$\frac{dG_i}{dy} = \frac{d\mu_i}{dy} + M_i g = 0 \qquad (11\text{-}71)$$

The derivative of $G$ vanishing is the same as $G$ having a constant value for each slab. For a perfect gas we can write

$$\mu_i = \mu_{i0} + RT \ln C_i \qquad (11\text{-}72)$$

If we substitute Equation (11-72) into Equation (11-71), we can write

$$RT \frac{d(\ln C_i)}{dy} = -M_i g \qquad (11\text{-}73)$$

This equation may be directly integrated and solved for the boundary condition that the concentration has a value $C_{i0}$ at the bottom of the column, that is, when $y = 0$. The result expression is

$$\frac{C_i}{C_{i0}} = e^{-M_i g y / RT} \qquad (11\text{-}74)$$

Since we are dealing with perfect gases, we can replace the ratio of concentrations with the ratio of pressures:

$$\frac{P_i}{P_{i0}} = \frac{C_i}{C_{i0}} = e^{-M_i g y / RT} \qquad (11\text{-}75)$$

The pressure decreases exponentially as a function of height. Equation (11-75) constitutes a complete solution to the problem.

To formulate the problem in classical statistical mechanics, we form an ensemble in which the members are perfect-gas molecules in a gravitational field and in contact with a reservoir at temperature $T$. The energy of each ensemble member is $mgy$, where $m$ is the mass per atom. Applying the Maxwell–Boltzmann distribution law, we see that the number of molecules lying between $y$ and $y + dy$ is

$$dN = \frac{N_0 \, e^{-mgy/kT} \, dy}{\int_0^\infty e^{-mgy/kT} \, dy} \tag{11-76}$$

The ratio of the number of molecules in a slab at height $y$ to that in a slab at the bottom of the column is

$$\frac{dN(y)}{dN(0)} = \frac{P}{P_0} = \frac{N_0 \, e^{-mgy/kT} \, dy}{\int_0^\infty e^{-mgy/kT} \, dy} \bigg/ \frac{N_0 \, e^{-mg \times 0/kT} \, dy}{\int_0^\infty e^{-mgy/kT} \, dy} \tag{11-77}$$

$$= e^{-mg \, y/kT}$$

If the numerator and denominator of the exponent are each multiplied by Avogadro's number, we get

$$\frac{P_y}{P_0} = e^{-\mathcal{N}mgy/\mathcal{N}kT} = e^{Mgy/RT} \tag{11-78}$$

Equation (11-78) follows since $\mathcal{N}m$, Avogadro's number times the mass of a molecule, is the molecular weight, and $\mathcal{N}k$ is $R$, the gas constant, which is the product of Boltzmann's constant times Avogadro's number. Equation (11-78) is thus identical to Equation (11-75).

The third method of approaching the problem consists of considering the forces on a slab of gas of thickness $dy$. The three forces are (1) the force due to the pressure on the bottom of the slab, which is balanced by (2) the weight of the slab plus (3) the force due to the pressure exerted on the top (Figure 11-2). For unit area

$$P = dW + P + dP \tag{11-79}$$

Equation (11-79) follows by inspection from Figure 11-2. At equilibrium the forces acting upward on the slab are equal to the downward forces. The change in pressure can be represented by $(dP/dy) \, dy$ while the increment of weight $dW$ is density times acceleration times volume or $\rho g \, dy$. We can therefore reformulate Equation (11-79),

$$\rho g \, dy = -\frac{dP}{dy} \, dy \tag{11-80}$$

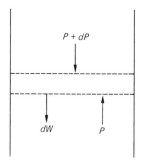

**Fig. 11-2.** A layer of gas from a standing isothermal column. At equilibrium the forces down, $P + dP + dW$, are just balanced by the force up, $P$.

The density is equal to $nM/V$, the numerator being mass (molecular weight times mole number), while $V$ is the volume. Using the perfect-gas law, we note that $n/V$ is equal to $P/RT$. Applying these factors to Equation (11-80) gives

$$\frac{PMg}{RT} = -\frac{dP}{dy} \tag{11-81}$$

This equation may be integrated subject to the boundary condition that $P = P_0$ at $y = 0$. The integrated equation is

$$P = P_0 e^{-Mgy/RT} \tag{11-82}$$

This is identical to the two solutions already obtained. The ability to derive this formula from varying points of view gives confidence in the conceptual structure we have been developing. It also serves to demonstrate the unity of the subject. Understanding the various methods of solving a problem gives insights into the meaning of the theory and the range of applicability.

PROBLEMS

1. Consider a new free-energy function $-(G - H - A)$. Discuss the properties of this function.

2. Suggest another term that might be added to Equation (11-14) in some problem of biological interest. Using the term, write the appropriate form of $dG$ for the problem being considered.

3. Express the Gibbs–Duhem relation [Equation (11-38)] as a function of activities for a two-component system. If we know the activity as a function of mole fraction for one component, show how we can determine this relation for the second component.

4. Derive Equation (11-63). Under what conditions is it valid?

5. A balloon has a volume of one liter and weighs 1 gm. Assuming that the atmosphere has an average molecular weight of 29, what height will the balloon ascend to at $300°K$?

CHAPTER **XII**

# Thermal Energy

*In all my travels through Milton's universes
I have not been able to escape completely from
the toils of chaos and its substrate, matter.
Heaven of Heavens seems in its ethereal
splendor farthest removed, but Satan discloses
as he mines its floor that it rests on chaotic
materials out of which its beauties have been
sublimated. Every physical property of Hell
bears upon it the signature of chaos.*

WALTER CLYDE CURRY
in "Milton's Ontology, Cosmogony
and Physics"
University of Kentucky Press, 1957

## A. ORDER AND DISORDER

Thermal energy, diffusion, Brownian motion, and noise are four
related topics of thermal physics which prove to be of great significance
in understanding much of biology in terms of its physical foundations.
From what has been said in previous chapters it is clear that all molecules and parts of molecules are in ceaseless thermal motion at all
temperatures other than absolute zero. Temperature at the molecular
level means the moving, twisting, turning, writhing, oscillating, and

*133*

general jumping around of molecular structures. Indeed, the one deceptive thing about the elegant accurately scaled atomic models that we build today is that they present us with a false static view of molecules. In drawing structures and building models, we tend to lose sight of the constant random motion which is a necessary part of the description of matter. This thermal energy is responsible for:

*a.* The decay of ordered systems to a state of maximum disorder or maximum entropy. As a result of the apparent randomness, hot spots develop and the existence of these hot spots leads to the breakdown of ordered structures. From the Maxwell–Boltzmann distribution we know that the probability of a molecular degree of freedom having an energy $E_c$ or greater is proportional to

$$\int_{E_c}^{\infty} e^{-E/kT} \, dE$$

If $E_c$ is large enough, such a molecule can on collision break covalent bonds and break down ordered structures. At thermal equilibrium molecules are constantly acquiring large amounts of kinetic energy. Consequently, the decay is ceaseless and can only be countered by doing the requisite work to rebuild the altered structures. The biosphere represents a kind of steady-state between the buildup of ordered macromolecular structures using photosynthetically acquired energy and the breakdown of these structures owing to random thermal noise.

*b. Chemical reactions.* In general for a reaction to occur the reacting species must have an energy $\Delta E$ in order to get over a potential-energy barrier. This $\Delta E$ comes from the kinetic energy of the two reacting species. The higher the temperature, the more molecules will have the requisite energy on collision and the faster the reaction will proceed. At absolute zero, chemical reactions do not take place.

*c. Diffusion.* If one examines the trajectory of a single molecule, there appears a type of random motion due to the thermal energy of the molecule and its collisions with other molecules. Such a trajectory is shown in Figure 12-1. If one has a collection of such molecules, a given molecule will have the same probability of moving from left to right as from right to left. Consequently, if there is a concentration difference between two neighboring points, there will be a net flow of molecules from the higher to the lower concentration. This random movement of molecules under a concentration gradient is called diffusion.

*d. Brownian motion.* A visible particle suspended in a liquid is observed to undergo an irregular trajectory similar to that shown in Figure 12-1. This motion results from the collision of large numbers of

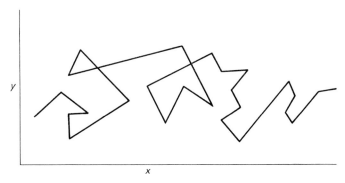

**Fig. 12-1.** The trajectory of a particle undergoing random thermal motion. Represented is a projection on the *xy*-plane.

liquid molecules with the particle. Since these collisions are random in nature and due to the thermal energy, at any instant there may be an imbalance of the force on one side of the particle compared to the opposite side. The motion under this force is Brownian motion. A collection of particles undergoing Brownian motion will also exhibit diffusion with a net flow from the higher to the lower concentration.

What the previous discussion has stressed is that at the atomic level things are very active and tend to get very disorderly. Erwin Schrödinger in his very perceptive book *What is Life?* stressed that most physical laws that we deal with are macroscopic and average over a sufficient number of molecules so that the type of disorder we have discussed does not invalidate the precision of the law. Only when we observe on a very micro scale, such as Brownian motion, do the random fluctuations come into play. Schrödinger then posed the following question: How do biological systems, which, in the limit, consist of events at a very micro level (a single molecule in the case of genetic events), manage to exhibit such orderly behavior under the ceaseless bombardment of random thermal energy? This question has not been completely answered, although our increasing knowledge of molecular biology and cellular control mechanisms suggests numerous ways out of the dilemma posed by Schrödinger. The rest of this chapter will examine in more detail a few aspects of thermal energy which prove to be of importance in biology.

## B. DIFFUSION

To begin the formal study of diffusion consider a membrane which is a plane slab of thickness $\Delta x$ containing regularly spaced holes which

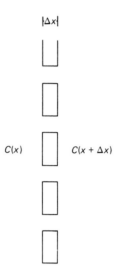

**Fig. 12-2.** Cross section through a membrane consisting of a plate of thickness $\Delta x$ with numerous holes through the plate.

are large in comparison with the size of diffusing molecules. On the left of the membrane the concentration of molecules at the membrane surface is $C(x)$ and on the right is $C(x + \Delta x)$ (Figure 12-2). The temperature is the same on both sides of the membrane. The flow of molecules across the membrane from left to right is proportional to $C_1$ and $\alpha$, the fraction of the membrane occupied by holes, and is inversely proportional to $\Delta x$, the thickness of the membrane, and directly proportional to the area of the flow $\mathscr{A}$ (empirical generalizations)

$$\text{Flow}(L \rightarrow R) = \frac{D\alpha C(x)\mathscr{A}}{\Delta x} \qquad (12\text{-}1)$$

where $D$ is the constant of proportionality. The flow from right to left can similarly be written as

$$\text{Flow}(R \rightarrow L) = \frac{D\alpha C(x + \Delta x)\mathscr{A}}{\Delta x} \qquad (12\text{-}2)$$

The net flow across the membrane is simply the difference between the two unidirectional flows,

$$\text{Net flow} = \frac{D\alpha C(x)\mathscr{A}}{\Delta x} - \frac{D\alpha C(x + \Delta x)\mathscr{A}}{\Delta x} \qquad (12\text{-}3)$$

Using the usual notation of the calculus, we can write $C(x + \Delta x) - C(x)$ as $\Delta C$, the increment in concentration across the membrane. In terms of this parameter, Equation (12-3) becomes

$$\text{Net flow} = -D\alpha \mathscr{A} \frac{\Delta C}{\Delta x} \qquad (12\text{-}4)$$

As $\Delta x$ becomes progressively smaller, the ratio $\Delta C/\Delta x$ approaches the derivative $dC/dx$ and we can write

$$\text{Net flow} = -D\alpha \frac{dC}{dx} \mathscr{A} \qquad (12\text{-}5)$$

As $\alpha$ approaches one, the pores become a progressively larger fraction of the area and the membrane effectively disappears from the picture and we are left with free diffusion. The rate of flow across an arbitrary plane is therefore

$$\text{Flow} = -D\mathscr{A} \frac{dC}{dx} \qquad (12\text{-}6)$$

Equation (12-6) applies to both gases and solutions, although the factors influencing $D$ are different in the two cases. The phenomenon described by the equation is based entirely on the random thermal motion of the molecules involved. $D$ is generally designated as the diffusion coefficient or the diffusion constant (although "constant" is often used, it is a rather poor descriptive name for a quantity which depends on many parameters of the system). For gases kinetic theory may be used to derive an expression for the diffusion coefficient in terms of molecular size, temperature, and various interaction parameters between molecules. For macromolecules in solution or particles suspended in liquids the diffusion coefficient can be related to the hydrodynamic properties of the particle, and this will be carried out in a later section.

Equation (12-6) can be introduced simply as a phenomenological equation (empirical generalization) and we can proceed on the basis of $D$ being a phenomenological coefficient. In this context it is known as Fick's first law of diffusion.

In our discussion of diffusion we will confine ourselves to the discussion of diffusion in one dimension. In each case the results can be generalized to three dimensions. This complicates the mathematics but does not introduce conceptual innovations. Since we are trying to expound concepts rather than to develop tools for the solution of specific problems, it seems sagacious to keep the formalism as simple as possible.

We will start with Equation (12-6) and derive a different form of the diffusion equation more useful in the solution of certain problems. Consider a slab of thickness $dx$ perpendicular to the $x$ axis (see Figure 12-3). Consider an area $\mathscr{A}$ of this slab. The diffusion flow into the slab

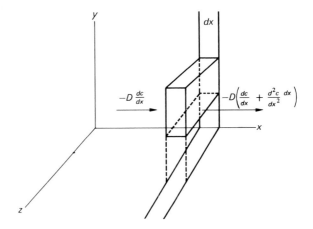

**Fig. 12-3.** Diffusion through a thin slab of thickness $dx$.

is given from Equation (12-6) as $- D\mathscr{A}\, dC/dx$. The diffusion flow across the corresponding face on the other side of the slab is given by the following equation:

$$\text{Flow} = - D\mathscr{A}\,\frac{dC(x + dx)}{dx} = - D\mathscr{A}\left[\frac{dC}{dx} + \frac{d^2C}{dx^2}\,dx\right] \qquad (12\text{-}7)$$

The net rate of change of the amount of material in the slab by diffusion is the flow in through the left-hand face minus the flow out through the right-hand face:

$$\text{Net rate of flow} = - D\mathscr{A}\,\frac{dC}{dx}\left[- D\mathscr{A}\left(\frac{dC}{dx} + \frac{d^2C}{dx^2}dx\right)\right]$$

$$= D\mathscr{A}\,\frac{d^2C}{dx^2}\,dx \qquad (12\text{-}8)$$

We can also calculate the rate of change of material in the slab by a different procedure. The quantity we wish to determine is the rate of change of mass of the diffusing component. But $M_d$, the mass of diffusing component in the segment of slab, is simply the concentration in mass units times the volume of the segment or $C\mathscr{A}/dx$. Since $\mathscr{A}$ and $dx$ are time-invariant, $dM_d/dt$ is $(dC/dt)\mathscr{A}\ dx$, which we can equate to Equation (11-8):

$$\frac{dC}{dt}\ \mathscr{A}\ dx = D\mathscr{A}\ \frac{d^2C}{dx^2}\ dx \qquad (12\text{-}9)$$

Dividing through by $\mathscr{A}\ dx$ yields

$$\frac{dC}{dt} = D\ \frac{d^2C}{dx^2} \qquad (12\text{-}10)$$

The above is known as the diffusion equation and is sometimes referred to as Fick's second law of diffusion. Equation (12-10) may now be used to estimate the distance that a particle or molecule will diffuse in a given time. Start with a plane source of particles. (This is an idealization; what we actually start with is a very thin slab located at the origin with a very high concentration of particles, which is in the center of a large container which has a zero concentration of particles at zero time.) What we require is a solution of Equation (12-10) that satisfies the following boundary conditions:

$$\begin{aligned} C &= \infty && \text{at}\quad x = 0, t = 0 \\ C &= 0 && \text{at}\quad x \neq 0, t = 0 \end{aligned} \qquad (12\text{-}11)$$

The time-dependent solution of Equation (12-10) then describes the outward movement of molecules from the initial very thin slab at zero time. We shall propose a solution and show that it has the required properties. The solution is

$$C = \frac{\Lambda}{t^{1/2}}\ e^{-x^2/4Dt} \qquad (12\text{-}12)$$

The coefficient $\Lambda$ is a constant of integration. To show that Equation (12-12) is indeed a solution, we must substitute it into Equation (12-10) and show that the resultant expression is an equality. This task is left to the reader in problem 1 at the end of this chapter. Anticipating the results, we note that

$$C(0, 0) = \frac{\Lambda e^{-0}}{(0)^{1/2}} = \infty \qquad (12\text{-}13)$$

This accords with our boundary conditions. For finite values of $x$ we must show that $C(x, 0)$ goes to zero. Rather than doing this analytically, which is somewhat difficult, let us assign $\Lambda$ and $-x^2/4D$ each values of 1 and examine the behavior of the function as $t \to 0$:

| $t$ | $C(x, t)$ |
|------|-----------|
| 1    | 0.367     |
| 0.25 | 0.0276    |
| 0.1  | 0.000135  |
| 0.01 | $10^{-42}$ |

The table demonstrates the point that the function also fits the second boundary condition, since for finite $x$ it very rapidly goes to zero as $t \to 0$.

The solution set of Equation (12-10) as a function of time is shown in Figure 12-4. The particles diffuse out uniformly, getting on the average

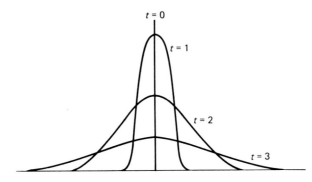

**Fig. 12-4.** The concentration of diffusing solute as a function of time. All the material is originally concentrated in a plane at the origin and spreads out in time.

farther and farther from the point of origin. We can use Equation (12-12) to calculate the average distance that a particle has diffused in time $t$. For reasons of mathematical convenience we will calculate the mean-square distance that a particle diffuses out from the origin. The fraction of particles lying in a plane slab between radii $x$ and $x + dx$ is

$$df(x, t) = \frac{C(x, t)\, dx}{\int_0^\infty C(x, t)\, dx} \tag{12-14}$$

The mean-square distance is given by

$$\overline{x^2} = \int_{-\infty}^{\infty} x^2\, df(x, t) = \frac{\int_{-\infty}^{\infty} x^2 C(x, t)\, dx}{\int_{-\infty}^{\infty} C(x, t)\, dx} \tag{12-15}$$

If we substitute Equation (12-12) into Equation (12-15) and integrate, we can evaluate $\overline{x^2}$ in terms of $D$ and $t$:

$$\overline{x^2} = 2Dt \tag{12-16}$$

Equation (12-16) is perfectly general, and applies in liquids and gases and under any conditions where the diffusion equation applies.

## C. BROWNIAN MOTION

We will now consider a more restrictive case, the random motion of particles which are large in comparison to the size of solvent molecules. This will apply to particles undergoing Brownian motion as well as to the diffusion of macromolecules such as proteins. For such particles we can use dynamical methods and write down the equation of motion

$$X(t) - f\dot{x} = m\ddot{x} \tag{12-17}$$

Equation (12-17) is just a statement of Newton's law that force is equal to mass times acceleration. Two forces act on each particle. The first is the random fluctuating force due to the thermal energy of solvent molecules that is, to unbalanced collisions with solvent molecules. The second is the frictional force which is experienced by any particle moving through a viscous fluid. The force is directed opposite to the velocity vector and for small velocities is given by $-fv$ where $v$ is the velocity, $\dot{x}$ in one dimension, and $f$ is the frictional coefficient. The quantity $f$ can in general be computed from hydrodynamics and for a sphere of radius $r$ it is $6\pi\eta r$, where $\eta$ is the coefficient of viscosity.

The approach we shall follow is to use Equation (12-17) to evaluate $\overline{x^2}$ by dynamical methods. We then compare the result to Equation (12-16) to see the meaning of the diffusion constant in terms of hydrodynamic variables. We begin by undertaking a set of transformations to recast Equation (12-17) in terms of $x^2$. We introduce a new variable $z = x^2$. It then follows that

$$\begin{aligned} \dot{z} &= 2x\dot{x} \\ \ddot{z} &= 2\dot{x}^2 + 2x\ddot{x} \end{aligned} \tag{12-18}$$

We then substitute (12-18) into (12-17):

$$X(t) - \frac{f\dot{z}}{2x} = \frac{m(\ddot{z} - 2\dot{x}^2)}{2x} \tag{12-19}$$

This may be rewritten as

$$\tfrac{1}{2}m\ddot{z} + \tfrac{1}{2}f\dot{z} + m\dot{x}^2 = xX(t) \tag{12-20}$$

The next step is to integrate the equation of motion with respect to time. (Note that $\dot{x}$ is the velocity of the particle, which we will represent as $v$.)

$$\tfrac{1}{2}m\dot{z} + \tfrac{1}{2}fz + \int_0^t mv^2\, dt = \int_0^t xX\, dt \tag{12-21}$$

Since the $X$ is a random fluctuating force, it will be uncorrelated with the displacement $x$, so that the right-hand side of Equation (12-21) is zero. We now have a differential equation in $x^2$, while we would like to evaluate $\overline{x^2}$, which is $x^2$ averaged over a large number of particles. The averaging leads to the following correspondence if we denote $x^2$ by $z$:

$$\begin{aligned}
\tfrac{1}{2}m\dot{z} &\to \tfrac{1}{2}m\dot{\bar{z}} \\
\tfrac{1}{2}fz &\to \tfrac{1}{2}f\bar{z} \\
\int_0^t mv^2\, dt &= \overline{mv^2}t = 2kTt
\end{aligned} \tag{12-22}$$

The first two transformations are obvious. The third comes about since the thermal energy of translation of a particle for any degree of freedom is $\tfrac{1}{2}kT$. These transformations lead to

$$\dot{\bar{z}} + \frac{f}{m}\,\bar{z} = \frac{2kTt}{m} \tag{12-23}$$

Equation (12-23) is a differential equation in $z$ which can be directly integrated to give

$$\bar{z} = \overline{x^2} = \chi e^{-(f/m)t} + \frac{2kT}{f}\left(t - \frac{m}{f}\right) \tag{12-24}$$

In usual cases encountered in biological application $f/m$ is large compared to the times of observation, so that the first and third terms vanish. We can examine the ratio $f/m$ for a sphere, for which $f$ is $6\pi\eta r$ and $m$ is $\tfrac{4}{3}\pi r^3\rho$, where $\rho$ is the density. The ratio is then $9\eta/2r^2\rho$. $\rho$ is the order of magnitude of one. $\eta$ for water at $20°$ is 0.01 in cgs units. The ratio is then $0.045r^{-2}$. For a one-micron particle this is 45,000 $sec^{-1}$, a very large number as pointed out above. Equation (12-24) then reduces to

$$\overline{x^2} = \frac{2kTt}{f} \tag{12-25}$$

We can now compare Equations (12-16) and (12-25). This leads to the result

$$D = \frac{kT}{f} \tag{12-26}$$

This equation relates Brownian motion, thermal energy, and the hydrodynamic properties of particles.

This brief chapter should serve to introduce the reader to the importance of random thermal motion in understanding the behavior of matter at the submicroscopic level. The reader interested in more details should consult a book like *Noise and Fluctuations: An Introduction* by D. K. C. MacDonald (Wiley, New York, 1962).

## PROBLEMS

1. Show by direct substitution that Equation (12-12) is a solution to Equation (12-10).

2. Ordinary macromolecules have a $D$ value of about $10^{-5}$ cm$^2$/sec. How long will it take for an average particle to diffuse one micron ($10^{-4}$ cm), 1 mm, 1 cm, 1 meter?

3. Calculate the diffusion coefficient of a one-micron-radius spherical particle.

# CHAPTER XIII

# Applications of
# the Gibbs Free Energy
# and the Gibbs Chemical Potential

*By combining the elements of chemistry
with the elements of cookery, we have found
it possible in our own experience to stimulate
interest and avoid repetition, thus saving a very
large amount of time for the student, and at the
same time to establish early the habit of seeking
a scientific explanation for each observation
made in everyday life.*

from " Chemistry and Cookery "

by A. L. MacLeod and E. H. Nason

McGraw-Hill Book Co.

## A. Electrochemistry

The formalism of the Gibbs free energy along with the concepts of
chemical potential and activity provide a framework for the solution of
a number of problems of biological and biochemical interest. While it
would clearly be too large a task to cover most of these, we will choose a
few selected examples to indicate the methods of approach and the kinds
of problems that can be handled.

*145*

A wide variety of chemical reactions can be carried out in such a manner so as to link the reaction to the flow of electricity in an external circuit. The setup is shown in Figure 13-1. The potentiometer provides a

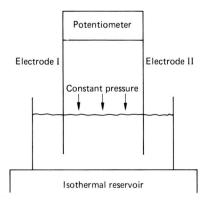

**Fig. 13-1.** Experimental set up for studying electrochemical reactions.

voltage equal to the voltage across the electrodes of the reaction vessels, so that there is no actual flow of current through the circuit at equilibrium. A slight increase of potentiometer voltage would cause current to flow in one direction through the reaction vessel and a slight decrease would cause current to flow in the other direction. Similarly, the linked chemical reaction going from reactants to products with the flow in one direction, will go from products to reactants with the flow in the other direction. This is very close to an idealized reversible situation and the ability to measure voltage with a high degree of precision makes this a choice method of obtaining thermodynamic data. The appropriate form of the free-energy function for this situation (see Chapter XI, Equation 11-14) is

$$dG = S\,dT - V\,dP + \sum \mu_i\,dn_i + \mathscr{E}\,de \qquad (13\text{-}1)$$

The conditions we wish to study are constant temperature and constant pressure. As previously indicated, for stoichiometric reactions the $dn_i$ are all related by

$$dn_i = v_i\,d\xi \qquad (13\text{-}2)$$

where the $v_i$ are the stoichiometric coefficients and $d\xi$ is the degree of advancement of the reaction. The flow of current is also linked to the degree of advancement, since electrode reactions are part of the process being described. Hence we can write

$$de = v_e \mathscr{F} \, d\xi \tag{13-3}$$

where $v_e$ is the number of moles of electrons flowing in the external circuit per unit reaction and $\mathscr{F}$ is the faraday, the number of coulombs of charge per mole of electrons. Equations (13-2) and (13-3) substituted into Equation (13-1) with the conditions of equilibrium ($dG = 0$) under isothermal ($dT = 0$) and isobaric ($dP = 0$) constraints yields

$$dG = \sum_i (\mu_i v_i + v_e \mathscr{E} \mathscr{F}) \, d\xi = 0 \tag{13-4}$$

Equation (13-4) can be met only if the coefficient of $d\xi$ vanishes:

$$\sum \mu_i v_i + v_e \mathscr{E} \mathscr{F} = 0 \tag{13-5}$$

Equation (13-5) is the fundamental equation of electrochemistry. It can be placed in a somewhat different form by utilizing the activity and replacing $\mu_i$ by $\mu_{i0} + RT \ln a_i$. This leads to

$$\sum v_i \mu_{i0} + RT \ln \prod_i a_i^{v_i} = -\mathscr{E} v_e \mathscr{F} \tag{13-6}$$

The first term on the left is $\Delta G_0$, the standard free energy of the reaction, and we proceed to define a quantity $\mathscr{E}_0$ which depends only on the reaction and is independent of the reaction conditions,

$$\mathscr{E}_0 = -\frac{\sum v_i \mu_{i0}}{v_e \mathscr{F}} = -\frac{\Delta G_0}{v_e \mathscr{F}} \tag{13-7}$$

We can thus rewrite Equation (13-6)

$$\mathscr{E} = \mathscr{E}_0 - \frac{RT}{v_e \mathscr{F}} \ln \prod_i a_i^{v_i} \tag{13-8}$$

Let us consider the following example to make the preceding theory more definite. For the reaction vessel of Figure (13-1), take a beaker of dilute hydrochloric acid in water. For electrode one, choose a hydrogen electrode, which is an activated piece of platinum against which a stream of hydrogen ($H_2$) bubbles is directed at 1 atm pressure. Electrode two is a silver wire coated with silver chloride. At electrode one the following reaction occurs:

$$\tfrac{1}{2} H_2(g) \rightleftharpoons H^+ + e^- \tag{13-9}$$

At electrode two the reaction is

$$AgCl(s) + e^- \rightleftharpoons Ag(s) + Cl^- \tag{13-10}$$

The overall chemical reaction is

$$\tfrac{1}{2}H_2(g) + AgCl(s) \rightleftharpoons H^+(c_1) + Cl^-(c_1) + Ag(s) \qquad (13\text{-}11)$$

In order for the reaction to occur, electrons must flow through an external circuit from the platinum electrode to the silver electrode. If the opposing voltage of the potentiometer is exactly $\mathscr{E}$, no current will flow and the system will be at equilibrium. One mole of electrons flows per unit of reaction as defined by Equation (13-11), so that $v_e$ is unity. Using Equations (13-11) and (13-8), we get

$$\mathscr{E} = \mathscr{E}_0 - \frac{RT}{\mathscr{F}} \ln \frac{a_{H^+}\, a_{Cl^-}\, a_{Ag}}{a_{H_2}^{1/2}\, a_{AgCl}} \qquad (13\text{-}12)$$

Since the standard state of $H_2$ is a gas at 1 atm pressure and the standard states of silver and silver chloride are the solids, $a_{H_2}$, $a_{Ag}$ and $a_{AgCl}$ are all unity. Equation (13-12) then reduces to the simple form

$$\mathscr{E} = \mathscr{E}_0 - \frac{RT}{\mathscr{F}} \ln a_{H^+}\, a_{Cl^-} \qquad (13\text{-}13)$$

If we choose an HCl solution such that $a_{H^+}$ and $a_{Cl^-}$ are unity, then we can directly measure the standard Gibbs free energy of the reaction. Alternatively, if we know $\mathscr{E}_0$, we can use the measurement of $\mathscr{E}$ to determine the activities of the $H^+$ and $Cl^-$ ions. In thermodynamic terms the *pH* of a solution can be defined as follows:

$$pH = -\ln a_{H^+} \qquad (13\text{-}14)$$

which allows us to write

$$\frac{\mathscr{F}(\mathscr{E} - \mathscr{E}_0)}{RT} + \ln a_{Cl} = pH \qquad (13\text{-}15)$$

Under the appropriate conditions this type of measurement can be used to measure *pH* and, indeed, *pH* meters involve standard electrodes and potentiometer circuits, and are based on this general method of approach.

To sum up the thermodynamic approach to electrochemistry, we note that the essential step was to add the electrical term to the expression for Gibbs free energy. Once this is done the stoichiometric equation for the electrode reactions had to be formulated. This led to Equation (13-8), which embodies the theoretical background. The hard work of electrochemistry consists in appropriate evaluation of activities, which is a major problem of solution chemistry. Indeed, it is often necessary to reconsider the electrodes and electrode reactions used in order to evaluate all the necessary experimental parameters.

## B. Surface Chemistry

We now proceed to a second case where the addition of a term to the Gibbs free energy allows us to explore another range of phenomena, in this case surface chemistry. We consider a system where the amount of energy involved in the formation of surfaces is of sufficient magnitude to be included in the total energy. The Gibbs free energy then becomes

$$dG = S\,dT - V\,dP + \sum_i \mu_i\,dn_i + \sigma\,d\mathscr{A} \qquad (13\text{-}16)$$

where $\sigma$ is the surface energy (the amount of energy required to change the surface of the system by one unit of area, all other quantities being held constant).

A simple and highly idealized case will illustrate the preceding, although an additional term must be considered. Suppose our system is a large spherical drop of pure liquid sitting on the bottom of a beaker as in Figure 13-2. If the droplet breaks up into smaller spherical droplets,

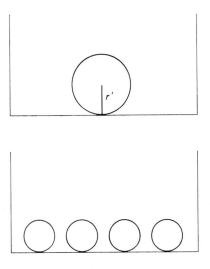

**Fig. 13-2.** Droplet of radius $r'$ on the bottom of a beaker. In the lower representation, the droplet breaks up into a number of smaller droplets.

it will decrease its gravitational energy and increase its surface energy. The problem is to determine the equilibrium droplet size. For this case we need to introduce the Gibbs free energy including gravitational and surface terms. At constant pressure and temperature this becomes

$$dG = d\mathscr{G} + \sigma \, d\mathscr{A} \tag{13-17}$$

If the initial droplet has a volume $V$ and density $\rho$, the mass is $V\rho$ and the gravitational potential when the droplets have a radius $r$ is

$$\mathscr{G} = V\rho r g \tag{13-18}$$

Each droplet acts with respect to gravitational potential as if its mass were concentrated at the center of the droplet. If the system breaks up into $N$ droplets, the area will be

$$\mathscr{A} = 4\pi r^2 N \tag{13-19}$$

Since the total volume must be conserved regardless of the droplet size, we can write

$$\tfrac{4}{3}\pi r^3 N = V \tag{13-20}$$

Combining (13-19) and (13-20), we can express the area in more convenient form as

$$\mathscr{A} = \frac{3V}{r} \tag{13-21}$$

If we now substitute Equations (13-18) and (13-21) into (13-17) and set $dG = 0$, which is the equilibrium condition, we get

$$dG = V\rho g \, dr - \frac{3V\sigma \, dr}{r^2} = 0 \tag{13-22}$$

Solving Equation (13-22) for the equilibrium radius, we get

$$r = \sqrt{\frac{3\sigma}{\rho g}} \tag{13-23}$$

Equation (13-23) is then a solution to our original problem. The equilibrium droplet size leads to a minimum Gibbs free energy for the system. This general type of analysis is applicable to colloidal suspensions and other problems where the surface-to-volume ratio is large enough to include terms involving surface energy.

Next move to a somewhat more complex surface problem where we need to consider both chemical potentials and surface terms. We wish to study the accumulation of dissolved molecules at surfaces.

For a system at constant temperature and pressure the Gibbs free energy equation becomes

$$dG = \sum \mu_i \, dn_i + \sigma \, d\mathscr{A} \tag{13-24}$$

To put the equation in a somewhat different form, we utilize the Gibbs–Duhem relation,

$$\sum \mu_i \, dn_i = -\sum n_i \, d\mu_i \tag{13-25}$$

Equations (13-24) and (13-25) then can be combined to make surface area and chemical potential the independent variables,

$$dG = \sigma \, d\mathscr{A} - \sum n_i \, d\mu_i \tag{13-26}$$

Since $G$ is a state function, we can express the coefficients of the differentials as partial derivatives of the free energy

$$\sigma = \left(\frac{\partial G}{\partial \mathscr{A}}\right)_{\mu_i}, \qquad -n_i = \left(\frac{\partial G}{\partial \mu_i}\right)_{\mathscr{A}} \tag{13-27}$$

Using the properties of partial differentials, we obtain

$$-\left(\frac{\partial n_i}{\partial \mathscr{A}}\right)_{\mu_i} = \left(\frac{\partial \sigma}{\partial \mu_i}\right)_{\mathscr{A}} \tag{13-28}$$

The quantity $\partial n_i/\partial \mathscr{A}$ is the amount of the $i$th substance that must be added or taken away in order to increase the area by an amount $d\mathscr{A}$ while keeping the bulk-phase chemical potential constant. It is called the surface excess $\Gamma_i$ (definition), for it is the amount of $i$th substance per unit area which either accumulates or depletes in order to minimize the free energy of the system. In order to see the significance of this quantity, substitute for $\mu_i$ in terms of the activity $a_i$ on the right-hand side of Equation (13-28):

$$\Gamma_i = -\frac{1}{RT} \frac{\partial \sigma}{\partial \ln a_i} \tag{13-29}$$

For dilute solutions approximate the activity by the concentration, so that Equation (13-29) becomes

$$\Gamma_i = -\frac{C_i}{RT} \frac{\partial \sigma}{\partial C_i} \tag{13-30}$$

Thus if $\partial\sigma/\partial C_i$ is negative, $\Gamma_i$ is positive; that is, solutes that lower the surface energy concentrate at the surface and solutes that raise the surface energy are depleted at the surface. Equation (13-30) is known as the Gibbs adsorption isotherm and is an effective example of the kind of problem which can be elucidated by the approach of the Gibbs free energy.

## C. THE PHASE RULE

Next we come to the phase rule which allows one to make certain predictions about multiphase multicomponent systems. If an equilibrium system exists in two phases (liquid–gas, liquid–liquid, solid–liquid, etc.) at constant temperature and pressure, then we can represent the chemical potential of the $i$th substance in the two phases as $\mu_{i_1}$ and $\mu_{i_2}$. At equilibrium the transfer of $dn$ moles from phase 1 to phase 2 will have a free-energy change of

$$dG = dn(\mu_2 - \mu_1) \tag{13-31}$$

Since the condition of equilibrium is a free-energy minimum, $dG$ must be zero and $\mu_1 = \mu_2$. The chemical potential must be the same in all phases. This can be seen to be generally true for any two phases in contact; if one of the components has a lower free energy in one phase than another, it will move into the lower phase and so lower the free energy of the entire system. Equilibrium can only exist when all components have the same chemical potential in all phases.

Assume that a system has $A$ phases and $B$ components. To specify each phase requires $B - 1$ composition variables (mole fractions—the reason for $B - 1$ rather than $B$ independent ones is that the mole fractions must add up to one). Therefore to completely specify the system requires $A(B - 1) + 2$ variables since we must also specify the temperature and pressure of the whole system. However, there are a number of restrictions which come about since the chemical potentials are equal in all phases and are themselves functions of the compositional variables, pressure, and temperature. Thus for each component there are $A - 1$ such relations and for all $B$ components there are $B(A - 1)$. Each of these may be used to eliminate one variable, so that we are left with the following expression for the number of independent variables:

$$A(B - 1) + 2 - B(A - 1) = B - A + 2 \tag{13-32}$$

The relationship between the number of independent variables or degrees of freedom and the number of phases and components is called the phase rule.

Consider some examples; for a pure substance which can exist in different phases, $B$ is 1 and the number of degrees of freedom is $3 - A$. For a one-phase system, there are $3 - 1$ or 2 degrees of freedom and any set of temperatures and pressures consistent with that phase can be maintained. For a two-phase system such as liquid and gas there are $3 - 2 = 1$ degree of freedom. If the temperature is specified, the vapor pressure of a solid or liquid system is completely determined. For a three-phase, one-component system there are $3 - 3$ or zero degrees of freedom; that is, there is a unique and completely determined triple point. In retrospect this is why the triple point of water proved to be such a good choice for a temperature standard.

Next consider a two-component system, which will then have $2 + 2 - A = 4 - A$ degrees of freedom. Where the two exist in one phase there are $4 - 1 = 3$ degrees of freedom—temperature, pressure, and mole fraction can be varied independently. Next consider the system existing in two phases (for definiteness think of a water–phenol system) such as liquid and gas. There are then $4 - 2 = 2$ degrees of freedom, so that if temperature and pressure are specified all compositional variables are fixed for both phases. Next consider three phases, such as gas and two immiscible liquid phases (two immiscible water–phenol phases in equilibrium with the vapor). There is then one degree of freedom, and once temperature is fixed all other variables are set. Numerous other applications have been made of the phase rule.

### D. OSMOTIC PRESSURE

Finally consider a thermodynamic treatment of osmotic pressure. A semipermeable membrane separates two compartments which are in contact with an isothermal reservoir. On the left-hand side of the membrane there is a pure solvent and on the right side is a solution using the same solvent as is on the left (Figure 13-3). The membrane is freely permeable to solvent and impermeable to solute. The left-hand compartment is at atmospheric pressure, while a pressure must be maintained on the right-hand compartment in order to maintain equilibrium; that is, to prevent the flow of solute across the membrane. Since the system is maintained at constant volume, the condition of equilibrium

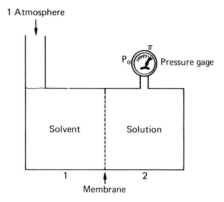

**Fig. 13-3.** Two compartments separated by a semipermeable membrane. The solvent is maintained at atmospheric pressure while the pressure of the solution rises to the osmotic pressure value $\Pi$.

is that the Helmholtz free energy be a minimum. At constant volume and temperature this condition reduces to

$$dA = \sum \mu_i \, dn_i = 0 \tag{13-33}$$

The only change $dn_i$ that is possible is the transport of $dn$ moles of solvent across the membrane:

$$dA = (\mu_2 - \mu_1) \, dn = 0 \tag{13-34}$$

The requirement for equilibrium is then that $\mu_2 = \mu_1$. The chemical potential of the solvent on the right side is given by

$$\mu_2 = \mu_0 + RT \ln a + \int_0^{\Pi} \left(\frac{\partial \mu}{\partial P}\right) dP \tag{13-35}$$

That is, we first formulate the chemical potential at standard pressure, and then formulate the change in chemical potential in going from the standard state to the final state at osmotic equilibrium. However, from the expression for the Helmholtz free energy, we can show that

$$\frac{\partial \mu_i}{\partial P} = \frac{\partial V}{\partial n_i} = \overline{V}_i \tag{13-36}$$

$\overline{V}_i$ is partial molar volume. To a first approximation it is a constant for most solvents. For perfect solutions we have already shown that the activity is equal to the mole fraction

$$a = \frac{n_{solvent}}{n_{solvent} + n_{solute}} \tag{13-37}$$

where the $n$'s are the numbers of moles. We can expand the activity term for dilute solutions as follows:

$$RT \ln a = -RT \ln \frac{1}{a} = -RT \ln\left(1 + \frac{n_{solute}}{n_{solvent}}\right)$$

$$= -RT \frac{n_{solute}}{n_{solvent}} \tag{13-38}$$

The chemical potential $\mu_1$ is $\mu_0$ since the solvent in the left-hand compartment is in its standard state (pure liquid at 1 atm pressure). We thus get the following relation, based on the equality of the chemical potential on both sides of the membrane:

$$\mu_0 = \mu_0 + RT \ln a + \int_0^\Pi \bar{V}\, dP \tag{13-39}$$

Using the results of Equation (13-38) and integrating the last term of Equation (13-39), we arrive at the following formulation:

$$RT \frac{n_{solute}}{n_{solvent}} = \Pi \bar{V} \tag{13-40}$$

For dilute solutions the volume of the entire system is very closely approximated by $n_{solvent}$ times $\bar{V}$. Therefore

$$\Pi V = n_{solute} RT \tag{13-41}$$

Equation (13-41) is the usual form for the osmotic pressure of dilute perfect solutions. It has been formulated entirely from thermodynamic arguments. The treatment once again exemplifies the utility of using free-energy functions for the solution of actual problems.

## PROBLEMS

1. Use the principles of Equation (13-15) to design a *pH* meter. Assume that you have calibration solutions of known *pH*.

2. A substance in solution breaks up into colloidal particles. The two

terms in the Gibbs free energy are entropy of mixing and surface energy. Derive an expression for the equilibrium radius of particles.

3. Some dissolved molecules spread as surface monolayers at air–water interfaces. Discuss this phenomenon in terms of Equation (13-30).

4. What is the maximum possible number of phases for a four-component system?

5. Show how osmotic-pressure measurements can be used to determine the molecular weight of a solute.

# CHAPTER XIV

# Measurement in Thermal Physics

*Methinks, Sancho, that there's no proverb*
*that is not true; for they are all sentences taken*
*out of experience itself, which is the universal*
*mother of sciences!*

from

"Don Quixote of the Mancha"

by MIGUEL DE CERVANTES

Since we have employed varying levels of abstraction throughout our discussion of thermodynamics, it is easy to lose sight of the fact that our formal structure ultimately rests on empirical generalizations and at each stage we must be able to relate our constructs to laboratory operations, experimental procedures which each of us can in principle carry out. In order to make our subject more concrete, it is worth pausing at this point and considering how measurements are actually made in thermal physics.

A consideration of the previous chapters will show that the empirical parameters of thermodynamics fall into two categories: those that are derivable from mechanics and analytical chemistry and those that are exclusively thermodynamic. Among the former are quantities like volume, pressure, surface tension, mass, density, mole number, gravitational potential, and many others. We will not discuss the measurement of these mechanical quantities, as we can take their measurement as something given apart from our considerations of thermodynamics.

The purely thermodynamic quantities all relate to the measurement of temperature and ultimately derive from the temperature scale. The measurement of energy is a mixed case. It is clear from our discussion of the measurability of internal energy that all energy measurement can be reduced to mechanical (electrical) terms; nevertheless, data are frequently expressed in calorimetric form, which is dependent on temperature measurement. This situation has been described by F. D. Rossini (*Chemical Thermodynamics*, Wiley, New York, 1950) as follows: " Notwithstanding the fact that practically all accurate calorimetric measurements made after about 1910 were actually based on electrical energy, most investigators continued until about 1930 to express their final results in such a way as to make it appear that the unit of energy was in some way still connected with the heat capacity of water. Actually, what they did was to convert their values, determined in international joules, into one or more of the several calories based on the heat capacity of water, usually for comparison with older values reported in calories in the literature. This procedure should have been reversed; that is, the older data should have been converted to the modern unit of energy."

Our task in this chapter is then threefold: (a) to discuss the experimental methods of measuring temperature; (b) to discuss the actual measurement of energy in thermodynamics and to relate the measures to calorimetric concepts; and (c) to discuss briefly the calorimeters and other devices which are used to determine thermochemical quantities such as heat of reaction, specific heats, thermal coefficients, and other parameters of interest.

By international agreement the triple point of water has a temperature of 273.16°K exactly. This triple point is produced for thermometric measurement using a triple-point cell as shown in Figure 14-1. The cells are glass cylinders 5 cm in diameter with reentrant coaxial walls for thermometers about 39 cm long and 1.3 cm in inside diameter. Extending up from the cell is a tube which is sealed off above the cell after filling. After very exhaustive cleaning the cell is filled with very-high-purity water to within about 2 cm of the top and is then sealed off. To prepare the cell for measurement, it is first immersed in an ice bath. One should note that since the triple point is only 0.0100 deg above the ice point, once the triple point is achieved there will be very little heat exchange between the cell and the bath. Crushed dry ice is then placed in the well until a mantle of ice 3–10 mm thick forms on the outside of the well.

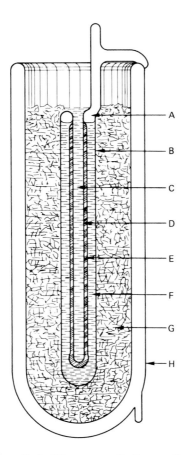

**Fig. 14-1.** Triple point cell. A: Water vapor, B: Pyrex cell; C: Water from ice bath; D: Thermometer well; E: Ice Mantle; F: Air-free water; G: Flaked ice and water; H: Insulated container.

The dry ice is then removed and the cell immersed below the water level of an ice bath so that ice-cold water fills the well. After equilibration the inner well constitutes a bath for thermometry at the triple point. These cells provide the experimental basis for the fixed point of the absolute thermodynamic temperature scale.

Given a fixed point, we next proceed to the fabrication of a thermometer. As we have proved in Appendix II, a perfect-gas thermometer should correspond to the Kelvin absolute thermodynamic scale. Such thermometers are in fact used for this purpose. A device of this type is used at the United States National Bureau of Standards and consists of a 500-cm$^3$ spherical shell made of platinum–20% rhodium. This bulb is immersed in a very elaborate furnace made of four concentric copper shells. The furnace is designed to maintain very constant temperature and to keep the pressure outside the bulb equal to that inside the bulb. The bulb connects to a precision mercury manometer which has a sensitivity of 2–3 m$\mu$ of mercury. Helium is generally the gas of choice in this type of thermometry, although extensive comparisons between gases have been carried out.

The two devices we have just outlined are in principle sufficient for complete thermometry. They are not particularly easy to use and are in general employed only in standards laboratories. In practice each temperature range has its measurement of choice and a number of secondary standards are introduced. Thus, below 1°K, the magnetic susceptibility of a paramagnetic substance such as chromic potassium alum is used for accurate temperature measurement. Between 1°K and 5.2°K, the vapor pressure of liquid helium has been used for thermometry. Platinum resistance thermometers are used over a wide temperature range.

Secondary standards are measured from the primary thermometric definitions and then used in practical thermometry. Thus the boiling point of oxygen is 90.168, the boiling point of water is 373.15, the boiling point of sulfur is 717.750, and the boiling point of silver is 1233.950.

For purposes of calorimetry the platinum resistance thermometer is probably the most frequently used measuring device. The instrument is in principle very simple and consists of very fine platinum wire usually helically wound on an electrically nonconducting rod. If the electrical resistance $R$ is known at some calibration temperature $T_0$ to be $R_0$, then we can always write an equation of the form

$$R = R_0 + R_1(T - T_0) + R_2(T - T_0)^2 + R_3(T - T_0)^3 \cdots \quad (14\text{-}1)$$

Equation (14-1) follows from the fact that any reasonably well behaved function can be approximated arbitrarily closely by a power-series expansion. Each available standard temperature allows the determination of one more coefficient in the expansion of Equation (14-1).

The usefulness of the platinum resistance thermometer is then determined by:

    a. The ease with which electrical resistance can be measured either by bridge circuits or potentiometric methods.

    b. The very high degree of accuracy with which electrical quantities can be measured.

c. The extremely good reproducibility of measurement of platinum coils.

The actual type of electrical measurement carried out varies considerably. To make the situation more concrete, consider the circuit in Figure 14-2. The thermometer is designated $R$ and is inserted in the

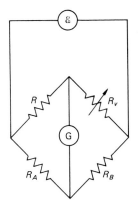

**Fig. 14-2.** Potentiometer circuit for a platinum resistance thermometer. $R$ is the thermometer and $\mathscr{E}$ is a constant applied voltage.

bridge circuit as shown. $\mathscr{E}$ is a very steady source of electrical potential such as a battery and $G$ is a galvanometer. $R_A$ and $R_B$ are two resistors of very precisely determined resistance. $R_v$ is a variable resistance which can be controlled with great accuracy. To take a measurement, the platinum coil is placed in contact with the object whose temperature is being measured. $R_v$ is then varied until the galvanometer reads no current. The condition for zero current is

$$\frac{R}{R_v} = \frac{R_A}{R_B} \qquad (14\text{-}2)$$

Since $R_A$, $R_B$, and $R_v$ are known with high precision, we have an accurate determination of $R$ and, by use of Equation (14-1), a precise measurement of temperature.

As already mentioned, in the actual present-day applications of thermodynamics the measure of energy depends upon the application of electrical measurements. National Standards Laboratories maintain standard cells and resistances so that the appropriate quantities may be measured in absolute volts and absolute ohms. When a voltage of one absolute volt is placed across a resistance of one absolute ohm for one second, the energy dissipated is one absolute joule. Measurements based on the absolute joule now form the basis of calorimetry, and data are converted into the older thermal nomenclature by the conversion factor: one calorie equals 4.1840 absolute joules. All thermodynamic energy measurements can now be stated in these standards.

Once having settled on the measurement of temperature and energy, we can now discuss the measurement of specific heats. This exemplifies a general class of thermodynamic measurements and at the same time is of special importance since the determination of absolute entropies is based on heat-capacity measurements.

A sample is placed in a cell with a heating coil and a platinum resistance thermometer. The cell is adiabatically isolated. In practice this can be achieved by placing the cell in the middle of an evacuated chamber to minimize conductive and convective heat transfer. Radiative transfer is minimized by keeping the chamber walls at the same temperature as the cell. This is done with a feedback circuit operating heating coils in the wall. A measured current is made to flow at a measured voltage through the heating coil for a measured time and the temperature is measured. This gives $\Delta Q/\Delta T$ or the heat capacity. The calorimeter must first be run without sample so that the heat capacity of the sample chamber can be computed and subtracted out. If the mass of the sample is then known, its specific heat can be computed. Variations of the apparatus are used over various temperature ranges but the basic principle of using the electrical measurements directly is usually followed.

Most of thermochemistry depends on the experimental determination of heats of reaction, of which the heat of combustion in oxygen is probably the most frequently used quantity. These reaction heats are determined in a bomb calorimeter. The reaction vessel or bomb is surrounded by a jacket of stirred calorimetric liquid, usually water. A weighed sample of substance is placed in the bomb along with high-pressure oxygen and the reaction is triggered with a hot electrical coil in the sample. The temperature rise of the calorimetric fluid is measured and this $\Delta T$ is a function of the heat of reaction. The calorimeter is calibrated either by reacting a standard substance of known $\Delta H$ or by heating the calorimetric liquid directly with a heating coil and measuring the temperature rise versus energy input as precisely determined from electrical measurements on the heater. For heats of combustion the most frequently used standard is the heat of combustion of benzoic acid of high purity. This material is supplied by the U.S. National Bureau of Standards and certified to have a combustion heat of $26.433_8$ absolute kilojoules per gram mass.

The actual carrying out of calorimetric experiments requires great care and the very brief outline we have presented does not indicate the elaborate experimental setup, the precise instrumentation, and the sophisticated computing programs which now go into the obtaining of thermodynamic data. The purpose of our survey has been to convey a sense of experimental reality to the concepts we have been discussing. Thermal physics, like all other sciences, stands or falls on experimental data, a fact which should always underlie the abstractions which are created to provide insightful analysis of the subject.

# CHAPTER XV

# Entropy and Biology

*It is not enough that you should understand about applied science in order that your work may increase man's blessings. Concern for man himself and his fate must always form the chief interest of all technical endeavors, concern for the great unsolved problems of the organization of labor and the distribution of goods —in order that the creations of our mind shall be a blessing and not a curse to mankind. Never forget this in the midst of your diagrams and equations.*

ALBERT EINSTEIN in a 1938
address to the student body
of California Institute of
Technology.

In previous chapters we have developed the relation between entropy and information. In this chapter we will explore some biological implications of this relation. We will proceed by a conceptual experiment which provides a focal point for our approach.

Assume that we start with a living cell: for purposes of concreteness we will choose a bacterial cell. The cell can be grown in nutrient medium to give rise to an arbitrarily large number of essentially identical cells. By essentially identical, we mean that they all have, to a rough approximation, the same genome, volume, energy, and the same atomic composition. If we now proceed to place each cell in a rigid adiabatic box of volume $V$, we will have an ensemble of isoenergetic systems. If we allow this ensemble to age for a very long time, all or most all of the cells will die, since a living cell is a very unlikely quantum state of the equilibrium system. In fact, in any real experiment that we could do it would be impossible to get enough cells to actually have any living cells in the final ensemble. What we are carrying out is a purely thought experiment since no ensemble on the surface of the earth could ever be large enough for our purposes. What will happen is that, as members of the ensemble age, the biochemical structures will break down and the various adiabatic boxes will be filled with $CO_2$, $CH_4$, graphite, $N_2$, and other breakdown products of the cell. The temperature of most boxes will rise since, as equilibrium is approached, much of the covalent bond energy will be converted to thermal energy. In any case we are led to the concept of an ensemble having the atomic composition, volume, and energy of a known living cell.

As already indicated, all quantum states of the same energy are assumed to have the same *a priori* probability of occurring in the ensemble. Suppose that for the ensemble under consideration there are $W$ possible quantum states and $X$ of these correspond to the system being a living cell. From the experimental failure of life to ever spontaneously generate in an equilibrium ensemble we can conclude that $W$ is very much greater than $X$:

$$W \gg X \tag{15-1}$$

The probability of an ensemble member being in a living state is $X/W$, so that the amount of information we have in knowing that a cell is alive is

$$I = -\ln_2 \frac{X}{W} \tag{15-2}$$

A somewhat more natural way of forming our ensemble would have been to isolate each cell in a rigid impermeable container and place it in contact with an infinite isothermal reservoir. The probability of such an ensemble member being alive would then be given by

$$p_a = \frac{\sum_i \delta_{ia} e^{-\varepsilon_i/kT}}{\sum e^{-\varepsilon_i/kT}} \tag{15-3}$$

The symbol $\delta_{ia}$ is similar to the Kronecker $\delta$ and has a value one if the $i$th state is alive and a value zero if the $i$th state is not alive. Equation (15-3) follows directly from Equation (9-15) of Chapter IX, where the $\varepsilon_i$ represent eigenenergies of all possible quantum states of the system. Now, all living states will have very close to the same energy, which we will designate as $\varepsilon_a$. If there are $X$ such states and if we represent the partition function as $Z$, we can rewrite Equation (15-3) as

$$p_a = \frac{X e^{-\varepsilon_a/kT}}{Z} \tag{15-4}$$

The information content in knowing that a cell is alive is then

$$I = -\ln_2 p_a = -\frac{\ln p_a}{0.693}. \tag{15-5}$$

Equation (15-4) converts from the logarithm to the base 2 to the logarithm to the base e, so that we can immediately substitute Equation (15-3) into equation (15-4) and get

$$I = \frac{1}{0.693}\left[\frac{\varepsilon_a}{kT} - \ln X + \ln Z\right] \tag{15-6}$$

If we now utilize Equations (9-24) qnd (9-25) of Chapter IX, which give the relationship between Helmholtz free energy, partition function, and the other thermodynamic functions, we see that

$$I = \frac{1}{0.693}\left[\frac{\varepsilon_a - kT \ln X - U + TS}{kT}\right] \tag{15-7}$$

Equation (15-7) may be rewritten as

$$I = \frac{1}{0.693}\left[\left(\frac{\varepsilon_a - U}{kT}\right) - \left(\frac{k \ln X - S}{k}\right)\right] \tag{15-8}$$

The information richness of the biological system (large $I$) comes from two factors in Equation (15-8), one of which we can comprehend relatively easily and the second of which remains something of a mystery from the point of view of physics. The first term involves $(\varepsilon_a - U)$, the difference in energy between the living system and an equilibrium system at the same temperature. Living systems are energy-rich. The process of photosynthesis leads to a storage of covalent bond energy. The difference $\varepsilon_a - U$ cannot be in thermal modes because it would very rapidly transfer to the reservoir if it existed as kinetic energy. The only way to maintain systems of the type we are discussing in an energy-rich stable state is to store the energy as potential energy of molecules.

The chemistry of the overall photosynthetic process is usually represented as

$$6CO_2 + 6H_2O \rightarrow C_6H_{12}O_6 + 6O_2 \qquad (15\text{-}9)$$

In terms of the actual process, Equation (15-9) is purely symbolic. It properly represents the reactants and products but neglects a very complex scheme of intermediate steps. The process is accompanied by the following changes in the various state functions (assuming the reactants and products are in their standard states):

$$\Delta G = -686.5 \text{ Kcal}$$

$$\Delta H = -669.9 \text{ Kcal}$$

$$\Delta S = \phantom{-}57 \quad \text{e.u.}$$

$$\Delta U = -673.1 \text{ Kcal}$$

The optical pumping of photosynthesis thus provides the $\varepsilon_a - U$; that is, this process brings the biosphere to a high potential energy, which accounts for the first term in Equation (15-8).

The second term, which may be rewritten $(S/k - \ln X)$, is always positive, as $S/k$ is large compared to $\ln X$. The reasoning is the same as that involved in Equation (15-1), that the total number of states is large compared with the number of living states. It is this term that is at the moment quite beyond the realm of thermodynamics since we have no real explanation of why, of all the possible quantum states, the biosphere is restricted to such a small subset. In any case, the first term in Equation (15-7) measures the energetic improbability and the second term represents the configurational improbability of the living state.

The very ordered state of a biological system would, if left to itself, decay to the most disordered possible state. For this reason work must constantly be performed to order the system. The continuous performance of this work requires a hot source and cold sink, which are ordinarily provided on the earth's surface by the heat of the sun and the cold of outer space.

Consider next the entropy changes which occur in the growth of a cell. The process we envision starts with a constant-volume flask containing sterile nutrient medium. The flask is in contact with an infinite isothermal reservoir. Into this flask we place a living cell and follow the processes which take place in cell growth and division so that the final product is two cells. The process may be represented as follows:

$$\text{cell} + \text{nutrients} \rightarrow 2 \text{ cells} + \text{waste products}$$

The initial cell emerges in the same state that it began in, so that it plays a catalytic role in the process and we can rewrite the previous scheme as

$$\text{nutrients} \rightarrow \text{cell} + \text{waste products}$$

This process will in general be accompanied by a transfer of heat to or from the reservoir. The entropy change can then be divided into two parts, the entropy change of the system and the entropy change of the reservoir:

$$\Delta S_{total} = \Delta S_{system} + \Delta S_{reservoir} > 0 \qquad (15\text{-}10)$$

Since the process is irreversible, we require that the total entropy change is positive. We may also write

$$\Delta S_{system} = S_{cells} + S_{waste\ products} - S_{nutrient}$$

$$\Delta S_{reservoir} = \frac{\Delta Q_{reservoir}}{T} = -\frac{\Delta Q_{system}}{T} \qquad (15\text{-}11)$$

*In actual cases cell growth appears to be exothermic* (empirical generalization). Equations (15-10) and (15-11) can be combined to give

$$\Delta S_{total} = \Delta S_{system} - \frac{\Delta Q_{system}}{T} > 0 \qquad (15\text{-}12)$$

As long as the total entropy change is positive, the growth of cells is an example of the operation of the second law of thermodynamics. The source in this case is the stored energy of the nutrients and the sink is the reservoir. Work is done in ordering the precursors into a cell.

At all levels life is very much subject to the second law of thermodynamics. The sun as a high-temperature source and outer space as a low-temperature sink provide two effectively infinite isothermal reservoirs for the continuous performance of work. On the surface of the earth a portion of that work continually goes into building up ordered biological structures out of simple molecules such as $CO_2$, $H_2O$, $N_2$, $NH_3$, etc. Dissipative processes inherent in the random distribution of thermal energy act to constantly degrade biological structures and return the material to the small molecule pool. This tension between photosynthetic buildup and thermal degradation drives the global processes of the biosphere and leads to the great ecological cycles. The entire process is exentropic owing to the flow of energy from the sun to outer space, but the local processes may lead to great order such as a rotifer, a sonnet, or the smile on the face of Mona Lisa.

# Conservation of Mechanical Energy: General Treatment

In order to generalize the mechanical development of the law of conservation of energy, it will first be necessary to present the briefest introduction to vector analysis, to become acquainted with the formal apparatus. In physics vectors are used to represent quantities which possess both magnitude and direction. Examples of such quantities are force and velocity. Quantities which have only magnitude are represented by numbers which are called scalars. Examples of scalar quantities are volume, temperature, and density. To distinguish vectors, we will represent them in boldface type such as the vector **F** for force.

In a Cartesian coordinate system we may represent a vector as a straight line beginning at the origin. Its length represents its magnitude while its position relative to the coordinate system represents its direction. A vector in a two-dimensional coordinate system is shown in Figure A1-1(a). Such a vector may also be represented by its projections

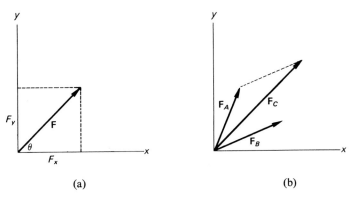

(a)                              (b)

*Fig. A1–1*

along the $x$ and $y$ axes, $F_x$ and $F_y$. Thus the magnitude of **F** is equal to $F_x^2 + F_y^2$ and the direction $\theta = \arctan F_y/F_x$. *Vector addition is accomplished by placing the tail of one vector adjacent to the arrow of the other, as shown in Figure A1-1b* (definition). Thus $\mathbf{F}_C = \mathbf{F}_A + \mathbf{F}_B$. In terms of the components it can be shown that

$$\mathbf{F}_{Cx} = \mathbf{F}_{Ax} + \mathbf{F}_{Bx}, \ \mathbf{F}_{Cy} = \mathbf{F}_{Ay} + \mathbf{F}_{By} \tag{A1-1}$$

The same reasoning can be extended to three dimensions as is indicated in Figure A1-2. We now introduce the concept of a unit vector,

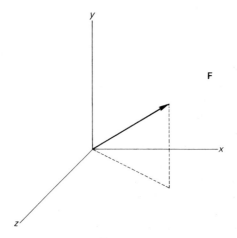

**Fig. A1–2**

a vector which has a magnitude of one in whatever units are used for the coordinate system. Any vector may be written as $F\mathbf{u}$, where $\mathbf{u}$ is a unit vector, which establishes direction, and $F$ is a scalar coefficient, which establishes magnitude. If we represent unit vectors along the $x$, $y$, and $z$ axes as $\mathbf{i}$, $\mathbf{j}$, and $\mathbf{k}$, we can then represent any vector as

$$\mathbf{F} = \mathbf{i}F_x + \mathbf{j}F_y + \mathbf{k}F_z \tag{A1-2}$$

Vector addition then becomes

$$\begin{aligned}\mathbf{F}_A + \mathbf{F}_B &= (\mathbf{i}F_{Ax} + \mathbf{j}F_{Ay} + \mathbf{k}F_{Az}) + (\mathbf{i}F_{Bx} + \mathbf{j}F_{By} + \mathbf{k}F_{Bz}) \\ &= \mathbf{i}(F_{Ax} + F_{Bx}) + \mathbf{j}(F_{Ay} + F_{By}) + \mathbf{k}(F_{Az} + F_{Bz})\end{aligned} \tag{A1-3}$$

As important quantity in a number of physical applications is *the scalar product of two vectors, which is a scalar quantity formed by multi-*

*plying the scalar magnitude of two vectors times the cosine of the angle between them* (definition). We represent the operation by a dot ($\cdot$) between the two vectors. As a result of this representation, the scalar product is sometimes referred to as the dot product of two vectors; thus

$$\mathbf{F} \cdot \mathbf{r} = Fr \cos \theta \qquad \text{(A1-4)}$$

If two vectors are parallel, the angle between them is $0°$, the cosine of zero is unity, and the scalar product is simply the product of their magnitudes. If two vectors are perpendicular, the angle is $90°$, the cosine of the angle is 0, and the scalar product is zero. Therefore

$$\mathbf{i} \cdot \mathbf{i} = \mathbf{j} \cdot \mathbf{j} = \mathbf{k} \cdot \mathbf{k} = 1 \qquad \text{(A1-5)}$$

$$\mathbf{i} \cdot \mathbf{j} = \mathbf{i} \cdot \mathbf{k} = \mathbf{j} \cdot \mathbf{k} = 0 \qquad \text{(A1-6)}$$

and

$$\mathbf{F} \cdot \mathbf{r} = (\mathbf{i}F_x + \mathbf{j}F_y + \mathbf{k}F_z) \cdot (\mathbf{i}r_x + \mathbf{j}r_y + \mathbf{k}r_z) \qquad \text{(A1-7)}$$
$$= F_x r_x + F_y r_y + F_z r_z$$

The scalar coefficients of vectors are subject to the ordinary rules of differentiation and integration. Consider the position vector $\mathbf{r}$, where

$$r_x = x, \qquad r_y = y, \qquad r_z = z \qquad \text{(A1-8)}$$

Then

$$\frac{d\mathbf{r}}{dt} = \mathbf{i}\frac{dx}{dt} + \mathbf{j}\frac{dy}{dt} + \mathbf{k}\frac{dz}{dt} \qquad \text{(A1-9)}$$

The derivative $d\mathbf{r}/dt$ is the velocity vector $\mathbf{v}$ and the second derivative $d^2\mathbf{r}/dt^2$ is the acceleration vector.

We will start our discussion of mechanics by assuming that the reader is familiar with the notions of force, position, velocity, and acceleration as vector quantities and the notion of mass as a scalar quantity. *The work done in moving a mass from one point to another is defined as the distance moved times the force directed along the line of motion* (definition). If the force is not entirely directed along the line of motion, we consider only its component in that direction, which is $F \cos \theta$ if $\theta$ is the angle between the force and line of motion. Since the force may change magnitude and direction along a path of motion, we must use differentials. Thus the amount of work in moving a distance $dr$ is

$$dW = F \cos \theta \, dr \qquad \text{(A1-10)}$$

However, as indicated in the last section, this can be represented in vector notation by

$$dW = \mathbf{F} \cdot d\mathbf{r} \tag{A1-11}$$

The amount of work done in moving an object from point $A$ to point $B$ is then given by

$$W_{AB} = \int_A^B \mathbf{F} \cdot d\mathbf{r} = \int_{x_A y_A z_A}^{x_B y_B z_B} F_x \, dx + F_y \, dy + F_z \, dz \tag{A1-12}$$

One of the interesting and most fundamental results of the study of mechanical systems is that *for such systems without friction $W_{AB}$ depends only on some function of the end points $x_A$, $y_A$, $z_A$, and $x_B$, $y_B$, $z_B$ and is independent of the path chosen to move the mass from A to B* (empirical generalization). Expressed in mathematical terms, this is

$$\int_{x_A y_A z_A}^{x_B y_B z_B} dW = \phi(x_B, y_B, z_B) - \phi(x_A, y_A, z_A) \tag{A1-13}$$

This result places certain purely mathematical restrictions on the function $W$ and demands that

$$dW = \frac{\partial W}{\partial x} \, dx + \frac{\partial W}{\partial y} \, dy + \frac{\partial W}{\partial z} \, dz \tag{A1-14}$$

But we already know that

$$dW = F_x \, dx + F_y \, dy + F_z \, dz \tag{A1-15}$$

Hence the following relations must hold:

$$F_x = \frac{\partial W}{\partial x}, \qquad F_y = \frac{\partial W}{\partial y}, \qquad F_z = \frac{\partial W}{\partial z} \tag{A1-16}$$

For reasons of convenience we do not use the function $W$, but the related function $V = -W$. Equation (A1-16) may then be written

$$F_x = -\frac{\partial V}{\partial x}, \qquad F_y = -\frac{\partial V}{\partial y}, \qquad F_z = -\frac{\partial V}{\partial z} \tag{A1-17}$$

*V is called the potential, and forces of the type first discussed are said to be derivable from a potential* (definition). *All of the usual forces of mechanics and electrostatics are of this form* (empirical generalization). The force vector may now be written

$$\mathbf{F} = -\mathbf{i} \frac{\partial V}{\partial x} - \mathbf{j} \frac{\partial V}{\partial y} - \mathbf{k} \frac{\partial V}{\partial z} \tag{A1-18}$$

We have now developed sufficient mathematical apparatus to undertake a generalized discussion of work from the point of view of Newton's second law of motion. In vector notation this law is

$$\mathbf{F} = m\frac{d^2\mathbf{r}}{dt^2} \tag{A1-19}$$

where $\mathbf{F}$ is the force on an object, $m$ its mass, and $d^2\mathbf{r}/dt^2$ is the acceleration.

When we introduce this expression for the force, as well as use Equation (A1-18) in Equation (A1-12), the resulting equation is

$$\int_{x_A y_A z_A}^{x_B y_B z_B} \mathbf{F} \cdot d\mathbf{r} = \int_{x_A y_A z_A}^{x_B y_B z_B} m\frac{d^2\mathbf{r}}{dt^2} \cdot d\mathbf{r}$$

$$= \int_{x_A y_A z_A}^{x_B y_B z_B} -\left(\frac{\partial V}{\partial x}dx + \frac{\partial V}{\partial y}dy + \frac{\partial V}{\partial z}dz\right) \tag{A1-20}$$

The middle and right-hand integrals can be rewritten in the following form:

$$\int_{x_A y_A z_A}^{x_B y_B z_B} m\frac{d(d\mathbf{r}/dt)}{dt} \cdot d\mathbf{r} = \int_{x_A y_A z_A}^{x_B y_B z_B} - dV \tag{A1-21}$$

As noted, following equation (A1-9), the velocity $\mathbf{v}$ is $d\mathbf{r}/dt$; therefore we can write

$$\int_{x_A y_A z_A}^{x_B y_B z_B} m\, d\mathbf{v} \cdot \mathbf{v} = V(x_A, y_A, z_A) - V(x_B, y_B, z_B) \tag{A1-22}$$

Equation (A1-22) may now be integrated to yield

$$\tfrac{1}{2}mv^2(x_B, y_B, z_B) - \tfrac{1}{2}mv^2(x_A, y_A, z_A) = V(x_A, y_A, z_A) - V(x_B, y_B, z_B) \tag{A1-23}$$

Equation (A1-23) may now be rewritten in the form

$$\tfrac{1}{2}mv^2(x_B, y_B, z_B) + V(x_B, y_B, z_B) = \tfrac{1}{2}mv^2(x_A, y_A, z_A) + V(x_A, y_A, z_A) \tag{A1-24}$$

The preceding equation is analogous to Equation (2-7) in Chapter II and expresses the law of conservation of mechanical energy in three-dimensional form.

# The Proof of the Equivalence
of the Perfect-Gas Temperature Scale
and the
Absolute Thermodynamic Temperature Scale

In order to proceed with this proof, we are required to develop two concepts in detail: (a) the equations of state of an ideal gas; and (b) the detailed nature of a reversible engine using an ideal gas as the sole working substance.

An ideal gas has previously been described as following the equation $PV = nR\theta$. One further feature of ideal gases is necessary for our subsequent treatment. This property of gases was first demonstrated in a free-expansion experiment. This experiment utilizes two chambers, one containing an ideal gas and the other under vacuum. The two chambers are enclosed in an adiabatic wall and a hole is opened between the two chambers. Initially the gas is at some $P_1$, $V_1$, $\theta_1$ and it finally equilibrates at $P_2$, $V_2$, $\theta_2$. The energy of a one-component system may be expressed as a function of any two state variables. So we have

$$U_1 = U(P_1, \theta_1) \tag{A2-1}$$
$$U_2 = U(P_2, \theta_2)$$

Because of the adiabatic isolation and the absence of any external work

$$U_1 = U_2 \tag{A2-2}$$

The experimental result of the free-expansion experiment is that $\theta_1 = \theta_2$; hence

$$U(P_1, \theta_1) = U(P_2, \theta_1) \tag{A2-3}$$

If we represent $U$ as a function of $V$ and $\theta$, we can similarly find

$$U(V_1, \theta_1) = U(V_2, \theta_1) \qquad (A2\text{-}4)$$

Since $P_2$ and $V_2$ are arbitrary, as the result is independent of the size of the two chambers, the preceding equations can only be satisfied if the internal energy of a perfect gas is a function of the temperature only. This condition can be expressed as

$$\left(\frac{\partial U}{\partial V}\right)_\theta = 0, \qquad \left(\frac{\partial U}{\partial P}\right)_\theta = 0 \qquad (A2\text{-}5)$$

We could have arrived at the same result from the point of view of kinetic theory. An ideal gas consists of molecules which have no potential energy of interaction except on collision. The total energy is thus the kinetic energy. From Chapter III, Equation (3-34), we see that the kinetic energy of each molecule is

$$\text{K.E.} = \tfrac{3}{2}k\theta \qquad (A2\text{-}6)$$

For a gas of $m$ molecules the total energy is thus

$$U = \tfrac{3}{2}mk\theta = U(\theta) \qquad (A2\text{-}7)$$

We next introduce the concept of specific heat $C$, which may be defined as

$$C = \frac{dQ}{d\theta} \qquad (A2\text{-}8)$$

It is the amount of heat which must be supplied to raise the temperature of the sample by 1 deg centigrade. In general we determine $dQ/d\theta$ under two conditions, that of constant pressure or constant volume. These specific heats are defined as

$$C_V = \left(\frac{\partial Q}{\partial \theta}\right)_V$$
$$C_P = \left(\frac{\partial Q}{\partial \theta}\right)_P \qquad (A2\text{-}9)$$

In general we may therefore write from the first law

$$dQ = dU + P\,dV \qquad (A2\text{-}10)$$

If Equation (A2-10) is substituted into Equation (A2-9), we get the following two expressions:

$$C_V = \left(\frac{\partial Q}{\partial \theta}\right)_V = \left(\frac{\partial U}{\partial \theta}\right)_V = \frac{dU}{d\theta} \tag{A2-11}$$

$$C_P = \frac{dU}{d\theta} + P\frac{dV}{d\theta} \tag{A2-12}$$

since $U$ is a function of $\theta$ only. Utilizing the perfect-gas law at constant pressure, we get

$$P\frac{dV}{d\theta} = nR \tag{A2-13}$$

Substituting this result into Equation (A2-12), we get the result that for perfect gases

$$C_P = C_V + nR \tag{A2-14}$$

The ratio of $C_P$ to $C_V$ is usually designated $\gamma$.

Consider next the equations for an adiabatic process in an ideal gas. Two equations must obtain, the first indicating an adiabatic process $(dQ = 0)$.

$$dQ = dU + P\,dV = 0 \tag{A2-15}$$

and the second indicating an ideal gas

$$PV = nRT \tag{A2-16}$$

We may utilize an accessory condition that for ideal gases $U$ is a function of $\theta$ only,

$$dU = \left(\frac{\partial U}{\partial \theta}\right)_V d\theta = C_V\,d\theta \tag{A2-17}$$

Expressing the perfect-gas law in differential form we get

$$P\,dV + V\,dP = nR\,d\theta \tag{A2-18}$$

We can now combine Equations (A2-15), (A2-17), and (A2-18) to get

$$C_V\frac{(P\,dV + V\,dP)}{nR} + P\,dV = 0 \tag{A2-19}$$

Placing terms over a common denominator and grouping coefficients, we can write the equation as

$$(C_V + nR)P \, dV + C_V V \, dP = 0 \qquad \text{(A2-20)}$$

Since $C_V + nR = C_P$, we can write

$$\frac{C_P}{C_V}\frac{dV}{V} + \frac{dP}{P} = \gamma \frac{dV}{V} + \frac{dP}{P} = 0 \qquad \text{(A2-21)}$$

Integrating this equation leads to

$$\gamma \ln V + \ln P = \text{constant} \qquad \text{(A2-22)}$$

$$\ln V^\gamma + \ln P = \ln PV^\gamma = \text{constant} \qquad \text{(A2-23)}$$

$$PV^\gamma = \text{constant} \qquad \text{(A2-24)}$$

Equation (A2-24) thus describes a reversible adiabatic process in a perfect gas.

Consider next the simplest possible reversible engine containing a perfect gas. It consists of a cylinder and a gas communicating with the outside world through a piston, the cylinder having a diathermal wall which may be closed off by an adiabatic wall (Figure A2-1). At the

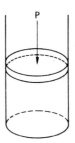

**Fig. A2–1**

beginning of the cycle the gas is at state $V_A$, $\theta_A$. Work is done by putting the cylinder in contact with an isothermal reservoir at temperature $\theta_A$ and allowing a reversible expansion to take place to state $P_B$, $V_B$, $\theta_B = \theta_A$. The work having been done, it is necessary to return the system to state $P_A$, $V_A$, $\theta_A$. In order to do this, the system is first adiabatically isolated and allowed to reversibly expand until the temperature drops to $\theta_C$, the temperature of the cold reservoir. These steps are shown on a $P$–$V$ diagram in Figure A2-2. The system is then placed in contact with

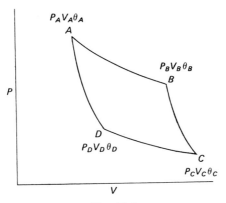

*Fig. A2–2*

a reservoir at temperature $\theta_C$ and isothermally compressed to $P_D$, $V_D$, $\theta_D = \theta_C$. The system is then returned to its original state by adiabatically isolating the cylinder and compressing the gas back to $P_A$, $V_A$, $\theta_A$. The total work done in going around the cycle is

$$W = \int_A^B P\,dV + \int_B^C P\,dV + \int_C^D P\,dV + \int_D^A P\,dV \qquad \text{(A2-25)}$$

An inspection of Figure A2-2 shows that this is just the area inside the curves $ABCD$.

The total heat taken from the hot reservoir is the integral of $P\,dV$ from $A$ to $B$. This is so since $\theta$ is constant and $U$ remains unchanged, so that the heat and work must balance in this expansion. This may be formally written as

$$Q_{AB} = \int_A^B P\,dV \qquad \text{(A2-26)}$$

The work done along the isothermals is

$$W = \int_{V_1}^{V_2} P\,dV = R\theta \int_{V_1}^{V_2} \frac{dV}{V} = R\theta \ln \frac{V_2}{V_1} \qquad \text{(A2-27)}$$

The work done along the adiabatics is

$$W = \int_{V_1}^{V_2} P\,dV = \text{const} \int_{V_1}^{V_2} \frac{dV}{V^\gamma} = \frac{\text{const}}{\gamma - 1}\left[\frac{1}{V_1^{\gamma-1}} - \frac{1}{V_2^{\gamma-1}}\right] \qquad \text{(A2-28)}$$

$$= \frac{1}{\gamma - 1}[P_1 V_1 - P_2 V_2]$$

The total work in going around the cycle is then

$$W = R\theta_A \ln \frac{V_B}{V_A} + R\theta_C \ln \frac{V_D}{V_C}$$

$$+ \frac{1}{\gamma - 1} [P_B V_B - P_C V_C + P_D V_D - P_A V_A] \qquad \text{(A2-29)}$$

The third term on the right is zero since

$$[P_B V_B - P_C V_C + P_D V_D - P_A V_A] = [R\theta_B - R\theta_C + R\theta_D - R\theta_A]$$

$$= R[(\theta_B - \theta_A) + (\theta_D - \theta_C)] = 0$$

$$\text{(A2-30)}$$

with the last term in brackets vanishing since $AB$ and $CD$ are isothermals so that $\theta_B = \theta_A$ and $\theta_D = \theta_C$. Therefore

$$W = R\theta_A \ln \frac{V_B}{V_A} + R\theta_C \ln \frac{V_D}{V_C} \qquad \text{(A2-31)}$$

The heat taken in is

$$Q_{AB} = R\theta_A \ln \frac{V_B}{V_A} \qquad \text{(A2-32)}$$

The equations of state in going around the cycle are

$$P_A V_A = P_B V_B$$
$$P_B V_B{}^\gamma = P_C V_C{}^\gamma \qquad \text{(A2-33)}$$
$$P_C V_C = P_D V_D$$
$$P_D V_D{}^\gamma = P_A V_A{}^\gamma$$

Eliminating the $P$'s from the preceding equations, we get

$$\frac{V_B}{V_A} = \frac{V_C}{V_D} \qquad \text{(A2-34)}$$

Substituting in Equation (A2-31), we get

$$W = R\theta_A \ln \frac{V_B}{V_A} + R\theta_C \ln \frac{V_D}{V_C} = R\theta_A \ln \frac{V_B}{V_A} + R\theta_C \ln \frac{V_A}{V_B} \qquad \text{(A2-35)}$$

This may be rewritten as

$$W = R\theta_A \ln \frac{V_B}{V_A} - R\theta_C \ln \frac{V_B}{V_A}$$

$$= \left(R \ln \frac{V_B}{V_A}\right)(\theta_A - \theta_C) \tag{A2-36}$$

The efficiency of the perfect gas engine is

$$\eta = \frac{W}{Q_{AB}} = \frac{[R \ln(V_B/V_A)](\theta_A - \theta_C)}{R\theta_A \ln(V_B/V_A)} = 1 - \frac{\theta_C}{\theta_A} \tag{A2-37}$$

The absolute thermodynamic temperature is defined from the relation

$$\eta = 1 - \frac{T_C}{T_A} \tag{A2-38}$$

Therefore

$$\frac{T_C}{T_A} = \frac{\theta_C}{\theta_A} \tag{A2-39}$$

# Entropy of a Perfect Gas

We start with the definition of entropy given in Equation (6-16) of Chapter VI:

$$dS = \frac{dU + P\,dV}{T} \tag{A3-1}$$

For a perfect gas we have the following relations:

$$U = U(T) = \tfrac{3}{2}nRT \tag{A3-2}$$

$$PV = nRT \tag{A3-3}$$

We can then substitute and get

$$dS = \frac{3}{2}nR\frac{dT}{T} + nR\frac{dV}{V} \tag{A3-4}$$

This equation can be directly integrated to give

$$S = \tfrac{3}{2}nR\ln T + nR\ln V + B \tag{A3-5}$$

($B$ = constant). Since $S$ is a function of $V$ and $T$ alone, it is clearly a function of state. We will now express $U$ as a function of $S$ and $V$:

$$\frac{S - B}{nR} = \ln VT^{3/2} \tag{A3-6}$$

Equation (A3-6) may be solved directly for $T$,

$$T = \left(\frac{e^{(S-B)/nR}}{V}\right)^{2/3} \tag{A3-7}$$

Since $U$ is a known function of $T$, we can do a direct substitution:

$$U = \frac{3}{2} nRT = \frac{3}{2} nR \left( \frac{e^{(S-B)/nR}}{V} \right)^{2/3} \tag{A3-8}$$

$$\left( \frac{\partial U}{\partial V} \right)_S = \frac{3}{2} nR (e^{(S-B)/nR})^{2/3} \left( \frac{-2}{3V^{5/3}} \right) \tag{A3-9}$$

Equations (A3-7) and (A3-3) can now be substituted into Equation (A3-9):

$$\left( \frac{\partial U}{\partial V} \right)_S = \frac{-nRT}{V} = -P \tag{A3-10}$$

$$\left( \frac{\partial U}{\partial S} \right)_V = \frac{3}{2} \frac{nR}{V^{2/3}} \frac{\partial e^{\frac{2}{3}(S-B)/nR}}{\partial S} \tag{A3-11}$$

$$\left( \frac{\partial U}{\partial S} \right)_V = \frac{3}{2} \frac{nR}{V^{2/3}} e^{\frac{2}{3}(S-B)/nR} \frac{2}{3nR} \tag{A3-12}$$

$$\left( \frac{\partial U}{\partial S} \right)_V = \left( \frac{e^{(S-B)/nR}}{V} \right)^{2/3} = T \tag{A3-13}$$

We have thus proven that for a perfect gas we can always find a function $S$ which satisfies the requirements that we have established.

# Stirling's Approximation

We wish to prove

$$\ln x! = x \ln x - x \qquad \text{(A4-1)}$$

Consider the left-hand side,

$$\ln x! = \sum_{n=1}^{x} \ln n \qquad \text{(A4-2)}$$

Graph $\ln n$ versus $n$ as in Figure A4-1.

The sum in Equation (A4-2) is the area under the solid line in Figure A4-1. This can be approximated by the area under the dotted

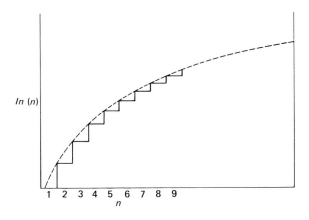

*In (n)*

1 2 3 4 5 6 7 8 9
*n*

**Fig. A4–1**

187

curve, which is $\int_1^x \ln n \, dn$. Therefore

$$\ln x! \cong \int_0^x \ln n \, dn = [n \ln n - n]_0^x \qquad \text{(A4-3)}$$

$$\ln x! \cong x \ln x - x \qquad \text{(A4-4)}$$

# Evaluation of the Partition Function of a Perfect Gas

We start out with Equation (9-29) of Chapter IX:

$$Z = \frac{1}{h^{3N}} \left[ \int \exp\left( -\frac{p_x^2 + p_y^2 + p_z^2}{2mkT} \right) dp_x \, dp_y \, dp_z \, dx \, dy \, dz \right]^N$$

(A5-1)

The integral over $dx \, dy \, dz$ is simply the volume of the system $V$. Equation (A5-1) may be simplified to give

$$Z = \frac{V^N}{h^{3N}} \left[ \int_{-\infty}^{\infty} \exp - \frac{p_x^2}{2mkT} \, dp_x \int_{-\infty}^{\infty} \exp - \frac{p_y^2}{2mkT} \, dp_y \right.$$
$$\left. \int_{-\infty}^{\infty} \exp - \frac{p_z^2}{2mkT} \, dp_z \right]^N$$

(A5-2)

Since all of the integrals in the bracket are identical, we can further simplify

$$Z = \frac{V^N}{h^{3N}} \left[ \int_{-\infty}^{\infty} \exp - \frac{p_x^2}{2mkT} \, dp_x \right]^{3N}$$

(A5-3)

The integral is a standard definite integral and can be shown to have the value

$$\int_{-\infty}^{\infty} \exp - \frac{p_x^2}{2mkT} \, dp_x = \sqrt{2\pi mkT}$$

(A5-4)

The partition function then becomes

$$Z = \left[ \frac{V}{h^3} (2\pi mkT)^{3/2} \right]^N$$

(A5-5)

# Index

# Index